The 245th Royal Academy of Arts Summer Exhibition

10 June – 18 August 2013

KT-415-646

Summer
Exhibition
List of Works
2013

Sponsored by

Royal Academy of Arts

Contents

Sponsor's Preface

Insight Investment is proud to continue its long association with the Royal Academy of Arts. It is a partnership that reflects shared values: the importance of striving to achieve excellence, the value of education and the potency of creative thinking.

Founded in 1768 under the patronage of King George III, the Royal Academy has become an influential part of the cultural life of the nation. The first Summer Exhibition was held one year after the Royal Academy was formed, and its objective was to create an exhibition open to all artists of merit that could be visited by the public. It has become the world's largest open exhibition and an established part of the summer social calendar.

This is Insight Investment's eighth year as the lead sponsor of the Summer Exhibition – a sponsorship that is almost as long as our short history. In a little over a decade Insight has grown into one of the largest asset managers in the UK. This record of growth has been achieved by following a simple philosophy. We listen carefully to what our clients want to achieve. Only then do we propose an investment solution, one which is unencumbered by a legacy mind-set. Our clients include pension funds, insurers, companies, sovereign wealth funds and individuals.

On the walls and around the galleries at the Summer Exhibition you will see works from British and international artists. The diversity is remarkable, but what all artists share is a commitment to creative self-expression.

Artistic inspiration is a potent part of the human experience. At Insight Investment we hope all visitors to the Summer Exhibition will be inspired by the passion and creativity on display.

Abdallah Nauphal
Chief Executive Officer

Insight
INVESTMENT

➤ A BNY MELLON COMPANY℠

Royal Academy of Arts in London, 2013

Registered Charity No. 1125383. Registered as a company limited by guarantee in England and Wales under Company No. 6298947

6

Michael Craig-Martin CBE
Gus Cummins
Richard Deacon CBE
Tacita Dean OBE
Spencer de Grey CBE
* Anne Desmet
Kenneth Draper
Jennifer Durrant
Prof Tracey Emin CBE
Prof Stephen Farthing
* Peter Freeth
Antony Gormley OBE
Prof Piers Gough CBE
Anthony Green
Sir Nicholas Grimshaw CBE PPRA
Dame Zaha Hadid DBE
Nigel Hall
Gary Hume
Prof Paul Huxley
Timothy Hyman
Bill Jacklin
Tess Jaray
* Eva Jiricna CBE
Allen Jones
Anish Kapoor CBE
Michael Landy
Christopher Le Brun PRA
Richard Long CBE
* Sir Richard MacCormac CBE
Jock McFadyen

Prof David Mach
Prof Ian McKeever
* John Maine
Lisa Milroy
Prof Dhruva Mistry CBE
Mick Moon
Mali Morris
David Nash OBE
* Prof Humphrey Ocean
Hughie O'Donoghue
Prof Chris Orr MBE
Cornelia Parker OBE
Eric Parry
Grayson Perry
Dr Barbara Rae CBE
Prof Fiona Rae
David Remfry MBE
Prof Ian Ritchie CBE
* Michael Rooney
Jenny Saville
Sean Scully
Alan Stanton
Emma Stibbon
Gillian Wearing OBE
Alison Wilding
Chris Wilkinson OBE
Prof Richard Wilson
Bill Woodrow
* John Wragg
* *Hanging Committee 2013*

Honorary Members

Antiquary: James Fenton
Chaplain: The Revd Lucy Winkett
Professor of Ancient History: Prof Sir
John Boardman FBA
Professor of Ancient Literature:
Prof Mary Beard OBE
Professor of History of Art:
Prof Dawn Ades CBE FBA
Professor of Law: The Rt Hon
Sir Alan Moses

Emeritus Professor of Law:
The Rt Hon Lord Hutchinson of
Lullington QC
Secretary for Foreign Correspondence:
The Rt Hon The Lord Carrington
KG GCMG CH MC PC
Corresponding Members:
Mrs Drue Heinz HON DBE
Sir Simon Robertson

7

8

9

Awards and Prizes

A total of £60,000 is offered in awards and prizes for every category of work in the Summer Exhibition

The Royal Academy of Arts Charles Wollaston Award
£25,000 to be awarded by a panel of judges appointed by the President and Council for the most distinguished work in the exhibition.

The Lend Lease/Architects' Journal Awards
£15,000 donated by Lend Lease: £10,000 Grand Award for Architecture; £5,000 for the best work by a first-time exhibitor in the Summer Exhibition.

The Jack Goldhill Award for Sculpture
£10,000 for a sculpture.

The Sunny Dupree Family Award for a Woman Artist
£3,500 for the best painting or sculpture.

The Arts Club Trust Award
£2,000 awarded to an artist aged 35 or under for a work in any medium except architecture.

The London Original Print Fair Prize
£2,500 for a print in any medium.

The Hugh Casson Drawing Prize
£1,500 for an original work on paper in any medium, where the emphasis is clearly on drawing.

The British Institution Awards
Four prizes of £1,000 each are awarded by the Trustees of the British Institution for Promoting the Fine Arts in the United Kingdom, which was established in 1805 to encourage the study of the fine arts. Students entering paintings, works on paper, sculpture and architecture will be eligible for the awards.

The Rose Award for Photography
£1,000 for a photograph or series of photographs.

Shepperd Robson Student Prize for Architecture
£5,000 for a student architectural work.

Submission and Sale of Works

The Summer Exhibition

The Royal Academy's Summer Exhibition is the largest open contemporary art exhibition in the world, drawing together a wide range of new work by both established and emerging living artists. Held annually since the Royal Academy's foundation in 1768, the Summer Exhibition is a unique showcase for art of all styles and media. An essential part of the London art calendar, the show draws over 150,000 visitors during its three-month run. Some 1,200 works are included and, following long Academy tradition, the exhibition is curated by an annually rotating committee of Royal Academicians, who are all practising artists and architects. The majority of works are for sale. Any artist may enter work for selection.

Entering works

An artist is entitled to submit a maximum of two works. If you are interested in entering work for next year's Summer Exhibition, details may be obtained from the Royal Academy's website, www.royalacademy.org.uk, from January 2014. Alternatively, please send a C5-sized stamped, addressed envelope to the Summer Exhibition Office, Royal Academy of Arts, Burlington House, Piccadilly, London W1J 0BD.

Sales of works

All prices are inclusive of VAT where applicable. Sold works are marked with red spots. The artist must pay the Royal Academy a commission of 30% plus VAT (the 'Commission') of the VAT-exclusive sales price of the work. The Royal Academy will take a deposit in an amount equal to the Commission from an intending purchaser on behalf of the artist when the offer to purchase is registered. The Royal Academy will apply the deposit in satisfaction of its Commission from the artist. Cheques, credit cards and cash are all acceptable. Upon notification by the Academy, the artist will contact the intending purchaser to formally accept the offer and request the balance of payment. If for any reason the artist does not accept the offer, the commission will be returned by the Royal Academy, on behalf of the artist. All arrangements for the payment of the balance and collection or delivery of the work are made between the artist and the purchaser. If the purchaser resides outside of the United Kingdom he or she must bear the transportation and importation costs. A VAT-registered artist is required to provide the purchaser with a VAT invoice.

Editions coming from abroad

Please be aware that purchasing editions by artists who live abroad may incur extra transportation/importation costs, and in this event these costs must be met by the purchaser. All artists' addresses are listed in the back of this book and are printed on the Offer to Purchase.

Collection of purchased works	All exhibited works must remain on display until the exhibition closes. Towards the close of the exhibition the artist, having received the balance of payment from the intending purchaser, will forward a signed Removal Order to the purchaser. The purchaser may collect the work from the Royal Academy on production of this card between Saturday 24 August and Friday 13 September 2013, Monday to Friday between 8 am and 4 pm, and on Saturdays between 9 am and 4 pm. Collection cannot be made on Sundays or on Monday 26 August (bank holiday).

The artist will send unframed editions of prints directly to the purchaser once the artist has received the balance of payment. |
| **Intellectual property rights** | Under the Copyright, Designs and Patents Act 1988 it is the general rule that, in the absence of any agreement to the contrary, copyright in a work of art belongs to the artist, or to his or her heirs and assigns. The artist also enjoys certain moral rights for the term of copyright, i.e. the rights of paternity and integrity. |
| **Academy Framing offer** | As a special offer, prints purchased from the Summer Exhibition will be framed, on production of the sales receipt, at a 15% discount on the normal cost of framing. |

Current and Future Exhibitions

Sir Hugh Casson PRA: Making Friends
Tennant Gallery
Until 25 August 2013

Mexico: A Revolution in Art, 1910–1940
Sackler Wing of Galleries
06 July – 29 September 2013

Richard Rogers RA: Inside Out
Burlington Gardens
18 July – 13 October 2013

John Carter RA
Tennant Gallery
04 September – 24 November 2013

AUSTRALIA
Main Galleries
21 September – 08 December 2013

Daumier
Sackler Wing of Galleries
26 October 2013 – 26 January 2014

Original Prints Glossary

An original print is created solely as a print, rather than being a reproduction of a work that exists in another medium. There are many ways of producing a print. Traditionally the image was transferred from a plate, block or stone onto paper, but many contemporary printmakers use a range of surfaces and often employ photographic and digital technologies.

The main printmaking techniques

Relief print The image is cut out of the block. The proud areas are inked and the image is transferred onto paper by press or hand.

Intaglio A plate is incised with an image, which is transferred to paper by a mangle-style press.

Lithography The image is produced on stone or zinc plates. Based on the principle that grease repels water, areas of the plate are made receptive to ink, while others remain blank in the printed image.

Screenprint The image is built up in layers by pushing ink through a mesh using a squeegee. This method is derived from commercial printing processes.

Digital print The image is created using computer software and is then printed using archival inks on high-quality paper.

Glossary of terms associated with prints

Aquatint A method that applies tonal areas to an etching, traditionally by adding rosin or asphalt to the plate before biting it in acid.

Artist's proof (A/P) Proofs made before the official print run, usually marked A/P.

Blind embossing An embossed image with no pigment, made by printing a plate that has not been inked.

Carborundum print A method whereby the surface of the plate is built up using carborundum grit, which holds the ink and creates rich, dense tones.

Chine collé Thin paper is applied to the image during the printing process to add areas of colour.

Collagraph The plate is built up with materials such as card or fabric before being inked and printed in the intaglio method.

Counterprint This is created by passing a print, usually an etching, through the press a second time. This reverses the image and is useful when text is included in the work.

C type A digital or photographic print on high-quality paper.

Drypoint The image is scratched directly onto an etching plate, acetate or cardboard, creating a burr that results in a rich and fluffy line. The plate is then bitten in acid and printed.

Edition The number of impressions of the image that will be made. A print's individual number is usually denoted in pencil on the front or back of the print, e.g. 1/25.

Engraving An image is cut directly into the plate before printing using the intaglio method.

Etching Marks are drawn through a resist on a plate, traditionally wax. The plate is then bitten in acid, inked, and printed using the intaglio method.

Hand-colouring Colour, usually watercolour, which is applied to the image after printing.

Hard-ground etching An etching produced by scratching through the wax resist.

Inkjet A computer-based printing process that creates an image by applying ink onto paper.

Letterpress A relief-printing process historically used to reproduce text using block letters.

Linocut A method whereby areas of a piece of linoleum are cut away before printing the remaining surface as a relief print.

Mezzotint A rocker is used to give the plate, traditionally made of copper, an all-over tone. This prints the image in black before a scraper and burnisher are used to introduce light tones.

Monoprint A unique print produced by making additions to a basic image, or by printing it in different colours.

Monotype An image is created by ink being applied to or removed from a blank plate using brushes or rollers.

Photogravure A photomechanical process using a light-sensitive gelatin tissue that is exposed to a film positive and then etched. This results in a print with the detail and continuous tones of a photograph.

Photopolymer gravure A method of transferring a hand-produced or photographic image onto a pre-sensitised plate using ultraviolet light. The image is then printed using the intaglio technique.

Relief etching A process in which an etching plate is inked up by applying ink to the surface rather than into the pit grooves and lines. It is then printed as a relief print.

Soft-ground etching An etching produced by drawing onto a piece of paper that is in contact with a prepared etching plate. The pressure of the pencil on the paper removes the resist, and the plate is then bitten with acid before the image is printed.

Spit bite A method of producing subtle tones on an etching plate prepared with an aquatint.

Sugarlift A sugar-based solution is applied to an etching plate, which is then varnished and submerged in water, dissolving the original marks to reveal blank areas. Aquatint can be added to produce the effect of calligraphic brush strokes before the plate is bitten.

Woodblock or woodcut The image is cut or gouged into a plank of wood which has been cut along the grain. The light areas are removed and the image is surface-rolled and printed using the relief process.

Wood engraving The image is cut into a piece of hardwood, such as box, lemonwood or cherry. These images tend to be small in scale and highly detailed.

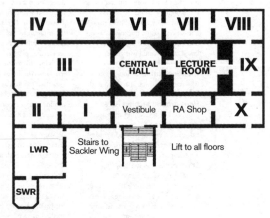

The Courtyard The Annenberg Courtyard
I Harry and Carol Djanogly Gallery
II Harry and Carol Djanogly Gallery
LWR Large Weston Room
SWR Small Weston Room
III The American Associates Gallery
IV
V The Jeanne Kahn Gallery
VI The Philip and Pauline Harris Gallery
Central Hall The Wohl Central Hall
VII The John Madejski Gallery
VIII The Weldon Gallery
IX The John A Roberts FRIBA Gallery
Lecture Room
X The Porter Gallery
The John Madejski Fine Rooms

Cloakrooms are
situated on the
ground floor

16

Catalogue

Courtyard

---

1 SETTLEMENT (A WORK IN THREE PARTS) *

*granite blocks (part one), portland roach and granite
(part two), granite monolith (part three)*

John Maine RA

---

2 UKRAINE £ 9,500

granite

John Maine RA

---

3 TSIATSIA – SEARCHING FOR CONNECTION *

*aluminium (bottle tops, printing plates, roofing sheets)
and copper wire*

El Anatsui

* *Refer to Sales Desk*

Wohl
Central Hall

---

4 IDENTICAL SHAPES: EIGHT ROWS £ 14,000

acrylic on plywood relief

John Carter RA

---

5 IDENTICAL SHAPES: TWO ROWS £ 450

screenprint

John Carter RA

(edition of 40: £350 each)

---

6 TREE £ 12,000

granite

John Maine RA

---

7 OPEN BLOCK £ 16,800

bronze

David Nash RA

(edition of 4: £16,800 each)

---

8 BEDROCK £ 12,000

Craiglash gneiss

John Maine RA

---

9 SCULPTURE BY ELEPHANTS £ 12,000

wood used by elephants to sharpen their tusks,
with thanks to London Zoo

Cornelia Parker RA

---

10 SHADOWS NFS

steel

Sir Anthony Caro RA

---

11 BLACKBURN £ 8,500

painted aluminium

Willard Boepple

---

12 SANCTUARY £ 45,000

granite

John Maine RA

---

13 REFLECTION, 1992 NFS
oil on board
The late Mary Fedden RA

14 BASKET OF GRAPES, 1999 NFS
oil
The late Mary Fedden RA

15 LORRY ART (PURCHASED BY THE ROYAL NFS
ACADEMY UNDER THE TERMS OF THE
CHANTREY BEQUEST)
oil
Rose Wylie

16 THE SPANISH CHOIR, 1988 NFS
oil
The late Mary Fedden RA

17 BLUE PLOUGH AND HORSE, 1977 NFS
oil on board
The late Mary Fedden RA

18 COWS IN A CHURCHYARD NFS
oil
The late Mary Fedden RA

19 FAVOURITE FLOWERS IN THE SILVER TANKARD £ 7,000
oil
Diana Armfield RA

20 OPEN DAY IN PENSFORD FIELD £ 6,000
oil
Diana Armfield RA

21 THE TETHERED GOAT, S. FRANCE £ 5,000
oil
Diana Armfield RA

22 CHAMBER MUSIC – WIGMORE HALL   £ 5,000
oil
Bernard Dunstan RA

23 COTTAGE BEDROOM   £ 7,000
oil
Bernard Dunstan RA

24 WELSH POPPIES FROM THE VERGE TO PARC   £ 7,000
oil
Diana Armfield RA

25 THE GATE LEFT OPEN, WINTER IN WALES   £ 7,000
oil
Diana Armfield RA

26 SITTING ON THE BED   £ 7,500
oil
Bernard Dunstan RA

27 A REHEARSAL   £ 7,000
oil
Bernard Dunstan RA

28 WINTER DAWN, TWO SHEEP IN THE LANE   £ 5,000
oil
Diana Armfield RA

29 ORVIETO: PIAZZA REPUBBLICA   £ 5,000
oil
Bernard Dunstan RA

30 REHEARSAL, VENICE   £ 6,500
oil
Bernard Dunstan RA

31 EVENING LANDSCAPE WITH TREE   £ 18,000
acrylic and collage
Anthony Whishaw RA

32 THE WAY WE SEE   £ 18,000
acrylic
Stephen Farthing RA

33 CHRISTCHURCH, SPITALFIELDS INTERIOR £ 7,000
pastel
Anthony Eyton RA

34 POTTING BENCH £ 4,000
oil
Olwyn Bowey RA

35 THE ANGEL OF THE SOUTH, DUNGENESS £ 20,000
oil
Frederick Cuming RA

36 DURANGO £ 4,000
acrylic
Mali Morris RA

37 DIXTER £ 33,000
oil
Gillian Ayres RA

38 STUDY FOR THE WAY WE SEE # 2 £ 9,000
oil
Stephen Farthing RA

39 SARAH AT ORIEL £ 50,000
oil
Ken Howard RA

40 LIVERPOOL STREET STATION CONCOURSE I £ 7,000
pastel
Anthony Eyton RA

41 SQUARE THE BLOCK £ 4,500
digital print, ink and card
Richard Wilson RA

42 SAILING INTO THE NIGHT £ 4,800
encaustic wax and oil on board
Terry Setch RA

43 ROCKS BY THE SEA, CORNWALL £ 8,000
oil
Leonard McComb RA

44 PURPLE TABLE AND ORANGE DISH £ 40,000
oil
Dame Elizabeth Blackadder RA

45 KNEELING BEFORE THE ALTAR OF THE UNKNOWN GOD £ 9,450
oil on wood
Timothy Hyman RA

46 HUMPHREY OCEAN £ 6,500
oil on card
Jock McFadyen RA

47 STONE DRY £ 24,000
acrylic
Frank Bowling RA

48 DOOR, BLUE, FOR KATHARINA (DIPTYCH) £ 21,000
work on panel
Tess Jaray RA

49 LAVA FIELD, KRAFLA £ 4,900
ink
Emma Stibbon RA

50 FUMAROLES, ICELAND £ 4,150
ink, mica and volcanic dust on paper
Emma Stibbon RA

51 UNTITLED £ 106,775
acrylic
Mimmo Paladino Hon RA

52 SEABIKES £ 4,900
encaustic wax and oil on metal
Terry Setch RA

53 SUNRISE ACROSS THE SEVERN £ 4,900
encaustic wax and oil on metal
Terry Setch RA

54 VIEWING BIG WAVES £ 5,000
encaustic wax and oil on metal
Terry Setch RA

55 SEABIKES AND YACHTS £ 4,900
encaustic wax and oil on metal
Terry Setch RA

56 DORIC SEA NFS
oil on linen
Sean Scully RA

57 HVERIR, ICELAND £ 4,700
ink and volcanic dust on paper
Emma Stibbon RA

58 DOWNPATRICK £ 55,000
mixed media and acrylic
Barbara Rae RA

59 TIMES SQUARE AT NIGHT IV £ 40,000
oil
Bill Jacklin RA

60 STILL INTERIOR £ 8,200
acrylic and collage
Anthony Whishaw RA

61 DURANGO II £ 4,800
acrylic
Mali Morris RA

62 THE WING BELOW THE ALPS £ 6,300
oil on board
Timothy Hyman RA

63 WILBURY £ 5,000
acrylic
Mali Morris RA

64 EVERYTHING MEETS HERE £ 7,200
pencil
Jessie Brennan

65 PASSION £ 5,500
oil
Jeffery Camp RA

66	**FLOWERING TREE**	£ 6,500
	oil	
	Jeffery Camp RA	

67	**DANDELION**	£ 4,000
	oil	
	Jeffery Camp RA	

68	**BUTTERFLY**	£ 4,000
	oil on board	
	Jeffery Camp RA	

69	**TULIPS**	£ 4,500
	oil	
	Jeffery Camp RA	

70	**BUDDLEIA**	£ 4,000
	oil	
	Jeffery Camp RA	

71	**NINE SONGS**	£ 22,000
	acrylic	
	Maurice Cockrill RA	

72	**BLACK KIMONO**	£ 30,000
	oil	
	Dame Elizabeth Blackadder RA	

73	**INNERSPACE**	£ 36,000
	acrylic	
	Frank Bowling RA	

74	**ARCHES, ADDIS ABABA STATION 2**	£ 20,000
	oil	
	Anthony Eyton RA	

75	**CELINALE**	£ 36,000
	oil	
	Gillian Ayres RA	

76	**TATE MOSS**	£ 55,000
	oil	
	Jock McFadyen RA	

77 THREE I £ 22,000
acrylic and oil
Ian McKeever RA

78 THREE II £ 22,000
acrylic and oil
Ian McKeever RA

79 THREE III £ 22,000
acrylic and oil
Ian McKeever RA

80 TRANSFORMATION OF THE AD NO. 2, O.631, FEB 1970 £ 57,600
oil
Alan Davie RA

81 FOUR OLD FRIENDS, OG.3538, 2012 £ 1,200
oil on paper
Alan Davie RA

82 NIGHT PHANTOM, OG.3460, 2012 £ 1,200
oil on paper
Alan Davie RA

83 TREE WITH 5 FLOWERS, OG.3461, 2013 £ 1,200
oil on paper
Alan Davie RA

84 NOVEMBER COMPILATION, O.2361, 2010 £ 15,600
oil
Alan Davie RA

85 FOR PATRICK (HIS VILLA) £ 7,200
acrylic
Mick Moon RA

86 UNGKAY £ 50,000
acrylic on museum board paper
Ed Ruscha Hon RA

87 NO BACK NO FRONT CAN GO UP OR DOWN £ 1,500
acrylic on wood
Lisa Milroy RA

88 UNTITLED (ARCHIVE) £ 11,800
acrylic and charcoal
Tony Bevan RA

89 BLUE EGG, O.2505, 2010 £ 3,600
oil on board
Alan Davie RA

90 ASHBERY RED £ 2,600
acrylic on MDF
Mali Morris RA

91 LU – GREEN III £ 18,000
acrylic
Paul Huxley RA

92 MUTATIS MUTANDIS XVI £ 18,000
acrylic
Paul Huxley RA

93 TORUS £ 18,000
acrylic
Paul Huxley RA

94 HUANG (YELLOW) £ 18,000
acrylic
Paul Huxley RA

95 ST KILDA FROM FLANNAN ISLES £ 48,000
oil and wax
Norman Ackroyd RA

96 HAPPY VALLEY NFS
oil on aluminium panel
Allen Jones RA

97 SELF-PORTRAIT £ 11,000
charcoal
Tony Bevan RA

98 ELEMENTAL HEAD: ST JAMES I £ 2,750
pencil on pondicherry paper
Stephen Cox RA

99 A BRIDGE IN BADEN-BADEN £ 26,000
watercolour
Michael Sandle RA

100 ELEMENTAL HEAD: ST JAMES II £ 2,750
pencil on pondicherry paper
Stephen Cox RA

101 SHIKANJI I £ 3,500
pastel on pondicherry paper
Stephen Cox RA

102 LAOKOON £ 250,000
oil
Per Kirkeby Hon RA

103 ISLINGTON NO. 4 £ 3,250
oil on board
Jock McFadyen RA

104 RED SOFA £ 3,500
oil on board
Jock McFadyen RA

105 AT HOME IN GLOBE ROAD £ 3,500
oil on board
Jock McFadyen RA

106 TRAFFIC £ 50,000
oil
Humphrey Ocean RA

107 STUDY FOR THE WAY WE SEE # 1 £ 9,000
oil
Stephen Farthing RA

108 LOUIS THE CAT AND JAPANESE PLATE £ 40,000
oil
Dame Elizabeth Blackadder RA

109 NOT WANTED ON VOYAGE £ 3,000
photo, inkjet print and ink
Richard Wilson RA

110 BACTRIAN CAMEL	£ 6,000
charcoal
Sir Anthony Caro RA

111 FROM THE ARABIAN NIGHTS	£ 39,000
oil
Tom Phillips RA

112 ETNA	£ 28,000
oil
Frederick Cuming RA

113 PC FROM VENICE SANTA MARIA DELLA VISITAZIONE	£ 45,000
acrylic on canvas on wood relief
Joe Tilson RA

114 ILLIUM	£ 36,000
oil
Gillian Ayres RA

115 STILL LIFE WITH PEARS AND PEACHES	£ 30,000
oil
Leonard McComb RA

116 SEA, SAND AND SHADOW	£ 3,250
monotype with acrylic, pencil and chalk
Ivor Abrahams RA

117 MASTER-PLAN	£ 12,000
oil and wax
Gus Cummins RA

118 PEACHES AGAINST A YELLOW GROUND	£ 8,000
oil
Leonard McComb RA

119 SNOWFLAKES	£ 4,800
encaustic wax and oil on board
Terry Setch RA

120 TREE AND PLANE IN SUNSHINE	£ 580
watercolour, pencil and ink on paper
Leonard Manasseh RA

121 SWEET AND SOUR £ 14,500
oil
Eileen Cooper RA

122 FREE THINKING £ 14,500
oil
Eileen Cooper RA

123 FLYING ABOVE £ 20,000
acrylic and collage
Anthony Whishaw RA

124 AXONS III £ 30,000
acrylic
Anthony Whishaw RA

125 NUDE £ 6,000
ink
Sir Anthony Caro RA

126 BACK DOOR STILL LIFE £ 4,000
tempera
David Tindle RA

127 WATER LEVELS £ 3,850
acrylic
Gus Cummins RA

128 CUMAE: LUNA £ 66,000
oil on linen
Hughie O'Donoghue RA

129 IN THE VALLEY £ 3,850
acrylic
Gus Cummins RA

130 TWO PIECES OF PAPER OF THE SAME SIZE £ 5,000
egg tempera on board
David Tindle RA

131 SEATED NUDE £ 6,000
charcoal
Sir Anthony Caro RA

132 PAPER PLANE £ 380
screenprint (artist's book)
Otto
(edition of 45: £95 each)

133 TORCHES £ 300
four-colour linocut
Steven Hubbard
(edition of 50: £250 each)

134 THE FAN £ 320
linocut
Steven Hubbard
(edition of 50: £270 each)

135 SILENT FOREST, FRIEDRICH AND TOHOKU £ 498
mixed media on paper
Kaori Homma
(edition of 5: £450 each)

136 27.3 TO 29.5 £ 3,800
laser engraved etching
Hen Coleman
(edition of 10: £3,000 each)

137 BETWEEN FOLDS, THEATRE POSTERS £ 5,900
paper (Theatre Royal's posters: 1929-1958)
Francisca Prieto

138 IT'S ALL FOR YOU £ 475
hand-cut digitally printed map
Claire Brewster
(edition of 20: £475 each)

139 A HUMUMENT P41: PICCADILLY GIRL £ 395
epson and screenprint
Tom Phillips RA
(edition of 100: £300 each)

140 A HUMUMENT P71: BOURGEOIS PICTURES £ 395
epson and screenprint
Tom Phillips RA
(edition of 100: £300 each)

141 MENU £ 500
digital print
Chris Kenny
(edition of 25: £395 each)

142 A COURSE IN SUSSEX II £ 1,075
epson and screenprint
Tom Phillips RA
(edition of 75: £900 each)

**143 CHICKENHAM, CHICKENS OF THE
WORLD UNITE!** £ 180
letterpress illustration print
Bobbie Jones
(edition of 40: £165 each)

144 LECOIN £ 950
mixed media
Kenneth Mahood

145 TULIPMANIA 10 £ 1,790
inket print with hand-painting
Gordon Cheung
(edition of 20: £1,440 each)

146 NORTH BRANCH £ 660
screenprint with woodblock
John Walker
(edition of 75: £480 each)

147 VARANASI £ 675
relief print and ink drawing on antique paper
Lauren Drescher
(edition of 15: £575 each)

148 TULIPMANIA 9 £ 1,790
inket print with hand-painting
Gordon Cheung
(edition of 20: £1,440 each)

149 VENICE (MOUTH OF ITALY) £ 31,200
ink and watercolour
Adam Dant

---

150 STUDY FOR A BATTLE £ 775
giclée print
Cathy de Monchaux
(edition of 75: £550 each)

---

151 ROCK, PAPER, SCISSORS £ 370
lithograph
James Seow
(edition of 25: £270 each)

---

152 A ROMANCE OF MANY DIMENSIONS £ 3,500
151 handcoloured copper plate etchings hand-cut
and layered into a bespoke box
Bella Easton & Iavor Lubomirov

---

153 PAST, PRESENT, FUTURE £ 3,000
sliced and folded book
Stiliana Alexieva

---

154 SILENT SPRING £ 3,500
printed feathers
Rebecca Jewell

---

155 FAGUS £ 480
etching
Buckmaster-French
(edition of 25: £480 each)

---

156 DIACONAT £ 950
mixed media
Kenneth Mahood

---

157 GOLD MAPPA MUNDI LONDON £ 3,200
screenprint with gold leaf
Ewan David Eason
(edition of 40: £2,800 each)

---

158 BETWEEN FOLDS, BRITISH BUTTERFLIES £ 9,200
paper (19th-century book)
Francisca Prieto

159 LAROUSSE UNIVERSEL, VOL. 2 £ 1,900
cut encyclopedia
Alexander Korzer-Robinson

160 LAROUSSE UNIVERSEL, VOL. 1 £ 1,900
cut encyclopedia
Alexander Korzer-Robinson

161 RIOBA: IL PAPA £ 1,200
carborundum
Hughie O'Donoghue RA
(edition of 25: £1,020 each)

162 GOING GREEN £ 695
etching
Margaret Sellars
(edition of 10: £550 each)

163 GOD'S WORLD I NFS
linocut
Jan Nowak

164 TRIPLE QUAY £ 250
wood engraving
Peter Lawrence
(edition of 25: £200 each)

165 UNTITLED £ 300
oil-based ink and graphite monoprint
Karen Williams

166 UNTITLED £ 300
oil-based ink and graphite monoprint
Karen Williams

167 STOLEN THUNDER £ 400
digital pigment print on photo rag 308gsm
Cornelia Parker RA
(edition of 100: £250 each)

168 CREATION I £ 210
screenprint
Anna Harley
(edition of 30: £150 each)

169 FIELD GAMES £ 2,700

woodcut on hand-made paper
Peter Ford
(edition of 4: £2,700 each)

170 STEEP DESCENT £ 410

colour woodcut
Irmgard Parth
(edition of 30: £360 each)

171 CLIFF VIEW £ 1,500

monotype with acrylic, pencil and chalk
Ivor Abrahams RA

172 ARIL £ 650

etching and thread on Japanese paper
Eleanor Havsteen-Franklin
(edition of 6: £560 each)

173 BORIS CROSSING THE THAMES £ 1,350

mixed media etching
Stephen Farthing RA
(edition of 4: £1,200 each)

174 RIOBA: RED NOSE £ 1,200

carborundum
Hughie O'Donoghue RA
(edition of 25: £1,020 each)

175 SATORIS £ 580

etching
Eleanor Havsteen-Franklin
(edition of 15: £480 each)

176 MIRAGE £ 550

etching on handmade paper
Peter Ford
(edition of 10: £420 each)

177 HER HANDS III £ 400

woodcut
Jean Lodge
(edition of 25: £360 each)

178 GIRL AND DOGS 2 £ 1,200
lithograph
Sir Quentin Blake
(edition of 30: £1,020 each)

179 JAG ROUNDS TOO £ 570
wood engraving and linocut
Edwina Ellis
(edition of 7: £450 each)

180 JAG ROUNDS ONE £ 720
wood engraving on polymer
Edwina Ellis
(edition of 3: £590 each)

181 AFTERNOON IN HAVANA £ 240
drypoint
Sally Loughridge
(edition of 12: £210 each)

182 TROUBLE IN THE DESIGN MUSEUM £ 1,100
letterpress gravure hand-tinted
Glen Baxter
(edition of 50: £950 each)

183 YOU FORGOT WHO YOU ARE £ 575
etching
Tracey Emin RA
(edition of 200: £375 each)

184 LOVE YOU £ 575
polymer gravure
Tracey Emin RA
(edition of 200: £375 each)

185 MAKING THINGS £ 170
etching
Mary Cossey
(edition of 50: £140 each)

186 RIG AND FURROW £ 310
screenprint
Hetty Haxworth
(edition of 20: £255 each)

187 SOLO NOIR   £ 850
silkscreen
Eileen Cooper RA
(edition of 60: £720 each)

188 GIRL AND DOGS 3   £ 1,200
lithograph
Sir Quentin Blake
(edition of 30: £1,020 each)

189 SHIM SHAM SHIMMY   £ 850
silkscreen
Eileen Cooper RA
(edition of 60: £720 each)

190 LOUIS   £ 1,120
etching
Dame Elizabeth Blackadder RA
(edition of 50: £960 each)

191 ART HISTORY CHART   £ 1,300
black pen on domestic colour chart
Nelly Dimitranova

192 GO FORWARD   £ 575
polymer gravure
Tracey Emin RA
(edition of 200: £375 each)

193 CUNNILINGUS   £ 650
etching
Tracey Emin RA
(edition of 100: £450 each)

194 CLOSED   £ 575
etching
Tracey Emin RA
(edition of 200: £375 each)

195 WE LOVE LONDON   £ 325
linocut
Mo Lancaster
(edition of 12: £290 each)

196	**RETURN**	£ 640

silkscreen
Eileen Cooper RA
(edition of 50: £550 each)

197	**TULIPS**	£ 2,350

screenprint
Dame Elizabeth Blackadder RA
(edition of 80: £2,160 each)

198	**IRISES**	£ 2,840

etching
Dame Elizabeth Blackadder RA
(edition of 50: £2,640 each)

199	**GIRL AND DOGS 1**	£ 1,200

lithograph
Sir Quentin Blake
(edition of 30: £1,020 each)

200	**PRIMEVAL**	£ 480

etching and gold leaf
Carmen Gracia
(edition of 25: £420 each)

201	**DESCANSO**	£ 1,440

woodcut
Gillian Ayres RA
(edition of 50: £1,200 each)

202	**ON LINE IV**	£ 450

etching with chine collé
Vanessa Jackson
(edition of 25: £360 each)

203	**ON LINE X**	£ 450

etching with chine collé
Vanessa Jackson
(edition of 25: £360 each)

204	**MOVING ABOUT, 2**	£ 145

etching
Olivia Krimpas
(edition of 15: £110 each)

205 POET £ 175
linocut and wood engraving
Luce
(edition of 25: £150 each)

---

206 FIESOLE £ 2,255
woodcut
Gillian Ayres RA
(edition of 35: £1,875 each)

---

207 XANADU £ 7,340
woodcut
Gillian Ayres RA
(edition of 15: £6,240 each)

---

208 FINESTRA VENEZIANA ZITA £ 2,880
aquatint
Joe Tilson RA
(edition of 60: £1,920 each)

---

209 PC FROM VENICE, SAN TROVASO, VENECIA £ 1,530
aquatint and collage
Joe Tilson RA
(edition of 20: £1,200 each)

---

210 PC FROM VENICE, SAN PANTALON, VENIESIA £ 1,530
aquatint and collage
Joe Tilson RA
(edition of 20: £1,200 each)

---

211 LITTLE BLUE PINOCCHIO £ 7,825
digital print and lithograph with hand-painting
Jim Dine
(edition of 12: £7,200 each)

---

212 SNIPS, PLIERS AND HAMMERS £ 13,920
woodcut and etching
Jim Dine
(edition of 15: £13,200 each)

---

213 FRIENDSHIP £ 2,610
screenprint with woodblock
Albert Irvin RA

214 SHAKESPEARE £ 2,610
screenprint
Albert Irvin RA

215 TWO PART INVENTION £ 1,890
lithograph
Allen Jones RA
(edition of 40: £1,080 each)

216 JUST LIKE THAT £ 1,890
lithograph
Allen Jones RA
(edition of 40: £1,080 each)

217 SWING LOW £ 1,890
lithograph
Allen Jones RA
(edition of 40: £1,080 each)

218 SUMMER VINEYARD £ 1,800
carborundum
Barbara Rae RA
(edition of 30: £1,500 each)

219 FAVEROT PATH £ 2,500
carborundum
Barbara Rae RA
(edition of 30: £2,000 each)

220 ACHILL FENCE £ 1,650
screenprint
Barbara Rae RA
(edition of 125: £1,200 each)

221 ACHILL BEACH £ 1,650
screenprint
Barbara Rae RA
(edition of 125: £1,200 each)

222 ST KILDA FROM FLANNAN £ 980
etching
Norman Ackroyd RA
(edition of 90: £800 each)

223 THE RUMBLINGS, MUCKLE FLUGGA, SHETLAND £ 980
etching
Norman Ackroyd RA
(edition of 90: £800 each)

224 BIG WORLD £ 1,800
etching with monoprint
Morgan Doyle

225 STACK – MANSTONE ROCK; STIPERSTONES, SHROPSHIRE £ 300
etching
David Harban
(edition of 10: £260 each)

226 BEYOND THE MOON £ 850
screenprint
Wuon-Gean Ho
(edition of 50: £650 each)

227 SMELLS OF RAIN £ 1,100
etching with monoprint
Morgan Doyle

228 FLATS £ 150
etching
Wendy Jacob
(edition of 30: £110 each)

229 THE STOUR IN WINTER £ 500
etching
Norman Ackroyd RA
(edition of 90: £400 each)

230 WIDFORD DAYBREAK £ 450
etching
Norman Ackroyd RA
(edition of 90: £350 each)

231 APPROACHING THE FLANNANS £ 450
etching
Norman Ackroyd RA
(edition of 90: £350 each)

232 INTERCHANGE/TRANSFORMATION £ 3,000
wood engraving and collage
Anne Desmet RA

233 2,000 YEARS OF STADIA £ 2,700
wood engravings printed on London map pages and
collaged onto roofing slate
Anne Desmet RA

234 OLYMPIC SITE MAP – METAMORPHOSIS £ 2,700
wood engravings printed on London map pages,
collaged on 75 ceramic tiles
Anne Desmet RA

235 CLIFF £ 150
etching
Wendy Jacob
(edition of 30: £110 each)

236 ON THE LEVEL £ 290
colour woodcut
Irmgard Parth
(edition of 40: £240 each)

237 THE GREAT ARCH £ 275
etching
Nicholas Richards
(edition of 50: £350 each)

238 POTENTIAL GOLD £ 1,900
wood engraving printed on paper and collaged onto
66 glass tesserae with gold leaf
Anne Desmet RA

239 FRAGILE HOPE £ 1,900
wood engravings printed on paper and collaged onto
6 razor shells
Anne Desmet RA

240 LONDON OLYMPIC AQUATICS CENTRE £ 370
wood engraving
Anne Desmet RA
(edition of 50: £250 each)

241 POSTPRINT NO 5, IL DILUVIO　£ 190
linocut and laser print with collage
Roy Willingham
(edition of 10: £140 each)

242 POSTPRINT NO 8, POSTO RECONDITO　£ 190
linocut with collage
Roy Willingham
(edition of 10: £140 each)

243 SCAFFOLDING ON THOMAS NORTH TERRACE　£ 195
engraving on plastic
Louise Hayward
(edition of 75: £170 each)

244 DEVON WINTER　£ 1,200
lithograph
Michael Honnor
(edition of 11: £950 each)

245 PARCEL FORCE, BRISTOL　£ 625
etching and aquatint
Ros Ford
(edition of 20: £395 each)

**246 ON THE ROAD TO DAMASCUS,
A LONDON FANTASY**　£ 2,300
engraving and stencil
Chris Orr RA
(edition of 20: £2,000 each)

**247 CUSTARD, CORSETS AND THE UNIVERSE,
LONDON'S PAST REVEALED**　£ 2,050
engraving, stencil and hand colouring
Chris Orr RA
(edition of 20: £1,750 each)

248 A VIEW OF DELFT　£ 1,075
lithography and screenprint
Chris Orr RA
(edition of 25: £900 each)

249 SLOANE SQUARE £ 570
hand-coloured lithograph
Adam Dant
(edition of 50: £420 each)

250 NOTES FROM THE UNDERGROUND £ 940
etching, aquatint and relief print
Mychael Barratt
(edition of 100: £790 each)

251 WATER WHEELS, HAMA £ 400
etching and aquatint
Joseph Winkelman
(edition of 100: £300 each)

252 VOYAGE £ 890
etching and hand-cut paper
Mila Fürstova
(edition of 20: £790 each)

253 SHARDCASTLE WEPT £ 850
etching and relief
Chris Orr RA
(edition of 30: £750 each)

254 CLASSIC TRAFFIC £ 170
etching and drypoint
Mike Tingle
(edition of 50: £110 each)

255 BIRDS ON A BEACH £ 150
etching and aquatint
Tim Southall
(edition of 75: £125 each)

256 THE PRINCESS HAS A PEA £ 800
lithograph and stencil
Chris Orr RA
(edition of 25: £700 each)

257 THE GOOD BAD £ 23,000
pigment and gold leaf
Stephen Chambers RA

258 UNTITLED (24TH)
linocut and screenprint
Sara Clark
(edition of 10: £200 each)

259 PICTORIAL MELODIES I
digital, drawing and screenprint
Jenny Wiener
(edition of 20: £425 each)

260 UNTITLED (19TH) £ 250
linocut and screenprint
Sara Clark
(edition of 10: £200 each)

261 THE PARTING £ 930
print-embossed screenprint
Jane Harris
(edition of 30: £750 each)

262 THREE STAGES OF MY LIFE £ 1,100
woodcut
Nana Shiomi
(edition of 30: £850 each)

263 UNTIL OTHER THERE £ 245
etching
Dolores de Sade
(edition of 20: £175 each)

264 A VISION OF A DESIGN AS A RUIN £ 545
hand-coloured etching
Dolores de Sade
(edition of 20: £385 each)

265 LIQUORICE WHIPPETS ON ECCLES SEA WALL £ 200
wood engraving
Neil Bousfield
(edition of 30: £160 each)

266 A HAPPISBURGH CARAVAN £ 200
wood engraving
Neil Bousfield
(edition of 30: £160 each)

267 CARNIVAL NFS
etching
Nikolai Batakov

268 ST FRANCIS OF ASSISI NFS
etching
Nikolai Batakov

269 DAPHNE & APOLLO £ 215
wood engraving
Jane Lydbury
(edition of 60: £195 each)

270 CONTEMPLATION £ 150
wood engraving
Rebecca Coleman
(edition of 250: £110 each)

271 CLIMBING THE STICKY LADDER II £ 350
etching and aquatint
Sumi Perera
(edition of 50: £300 each)

272 VIEW SUBTERRANEA 1 £ 160
wood engraving
Rebecca Coleman
(edition of 250: £120 each)

273 BOROUGH NIGHTFALL £ 190
linocut
Jennifer Jokhoo
(edition of 15: £145 each)

274 GARAN-DO, AUTUMN £ 1,100
woodcut
Nana Shiomi
(edition of 30: £850 each)

275 SAVE OUR ART SCHOOLS £ 750
screenprint
Leigh Clarke
(edition of 25: £600 each)

276 LIVERPOOL £ 675
linocut
Mike Hatjoullis
(edition of 30: £575 each)

277 TOWER OF THE WINDS VII £ 350
woodcut
Weimin He
(edition of 60: £290 each)

278 ANNECY – CÉZANNE AND JOHN SKETCHING £ 250
OUTSIDE THE CAFÉ DES ARTS
wood engraving
Peter Lawrence
(edition of 35: £200 each)

279 SHORETOISE £ 200
aquatint etching
Adam Wardle
(edition of 50: £150 each)

280 THE RIVER £ 130
wood engraving
Jonathan Gibbs
(edition of 50: £100 each)

281 MAN ON A MISSION £ 120
linocut
Adrian Bannister
(edition of 60: £85 each)

282 CLAVIE, FROM VERNACULAR VOCABULARIES £ 580
hand-coloured screenprint and text
Arthur Watson
(edition of 18: £450 each)

283 REFLECTIONS OF THE PLAYGROUND £ 395
etching and chine collé
Ann Manie

284 MOONRIDE, CORNWALL £ 160
copperplate engraving
Brian Hanscomb
(edition of 95: £120 each)

285 JUNGLE GARDENER £ 250
wood engraving
Ben Goodman
(edition of 20: £200 each)

286 THE ANAESTHETIST £ 800
etching
Freya Payne
(edition of 15: £650 each)

287 WORK II £ 250
etching
Jane Stobart
(edition of 15: £200 each)

288 A – ALBERT MEMORIAL (FROM THE £ 300
LONDON A–Z SERIES)
linocut
Tobias Till
(edition of 75: £200 each)

289 STRING FRAME £ 320
collagraph and block print
Katherine Jones
(edition of 50: £260 each)

290 SECOND SHADOW I £ 800
etching
Freya Payne
(edition of 15: £650 each)

291 AN AFFABLE IRREGULAR £ 395
etching
Anthony Connolly
(edition of 25: £275 each)

292 THE MEETING II £ 370
etching
Pieter Lerooij
(edition of 30: £350 each)

293 THE SHARD UNDER CONSTRUCTION £ 130
etching
Jacqueline Newell
(edition of 15: £90 each)

294 BLACKFRIARS BRIDGE UNDER CONSTRUCTION £ 130
etching
Jacqueline Newell
(edition of 15: £90 each)

295 THE CUT £ 350
archival digital print
Jessie Brennan
(edition of 25: £250 each)

296 LANDMARK: SILVERTOWN £ 165
mezzotint
Rosey Prince
(edition of 20: £130 each)

297 CHOPPER III £ 340
etching (soft ground)
Tamsin Relly
(edition of 20: £190 each)

298 SOUTH DOWNS £ 350
polymer intaglio
Christopher Knox
(edition of 60: £280 each)

299 CLOISTERS, GLOUCESTER £ 190
etching
Henry Hagger
(edition of 30: £150 each)

300 THRESHOLD £ 300
wood engraving
Peter S Smith
(edition of 20: £200 each)

301 THE DRYING ROOM £ 150
resingrave engraving
Geri Waddington
(edition of 100: £100 each)

302 FLY AGARICS £ 320
mezzotint
Konstantin Chmutin
(edition of 50: £270 each)

303 Q121, THE 24' WINDTUNNEL, FARNBOROUGH £ 220
hard ground etching and aquatint
Judy Nadal

304 TINY UNIVERSE, TWO HALVES £ 200
found sandpaper with paint traces
Marcia Teusink

305 PLAYGROUND UNDER CONSTRUCTION £ 395
etching and chine collé
Ann Manie

306 TERMINUS £ 5,000
etching
Clive Head
(edition of 30: £4,560 each)

307 REFUGE £ 525
woodcut, in the ukiyo-e tradition
Sara Lee
(edition of 25: £395 each)

308 UNTITLED (SOMETIMES) £ 440
screenprint
Liz Collini
(edition of 12: £380 each)

309 TREADING THE EDGE £ 575
woodcut
Sara Lee
(edition of 25: £425 each)

310 SCOTS PINE £ 175
etching
Guy Allen
(edition of 85: £125 each)

311 BELL JAR X £ 65
screenprint
Chitra Merchant
(edition of 100: £60 each)

312 BELL JAR VII £ 65
screenprint
Chitra Merchant
(edition of 50: £60 each)

313 RADIOLARIA, SYMMETRICAL CYLINDERS £ 2,800
high-fired unglazed porcelain
Nuala O'Donovan

314 GEOGRAPHY £ 1,500
book, string, glass and chipboard
Jadranka Bekavac-Kononenko

315 MULE MAKE MULE £ 22,000
mixed media construction
Tim Lewis

316 STADIUM URN £ 1,300
digitally printed stoneware
Alice Mara
(edition of 3)

317 COUNCIL FLATS £ 1,300
digitally printed stoneware
Alice Mara
(edition of 3)

318 SOHO RAIN £ 395
etching
John Duffin
(edition of 150: £295 each)

319 FLIGHT LEVEL 325 £ 255
collagraph
Anna Warsop
(edition of 18: £195 each)

320 COMMA COMPOSITION £ 1,800
typewriter on newsprint
Kasper Pincis

321 BAPTISM £ 295
etching
Paul Hawdon
(edition of 40: £255 each)

322 ADAM AND EVE £ 295
etching
Paul Hawdon
(edition of 40: £255 each)

323 WHO'S SORRY NOW? (FORTY WINKS IN £ 300
THE GARDEN)
aquatint
Peter Freeth RA
(edition of 45: £250 each)

324 THAT FORBIDDEN TREE £ 300
aquatint
Peter Freeth RA
(edition of 45: £250 each)

325 SNAKE YEAR £ 200
solar plate etching
Pamela Aldridge
(edition of 50: £150 each)

326 THE TASTY MEAL DEAL, AFTER PICASSO £ 325
woodcut
Gerry Baptist
(edition of 15: £250 each)

327 YOU CAN NEVER HAVE ENOUGH ART CAN YOU £ 500
digital print and screenprint
Mark Hampson
(edition of 40: £400 each)

Michael

328 ELECTRIC AVENUE, A CLOSER LOOK 1 £ 750
sugar lift etching
Simon Lawson
(edition of 20: £550 each)

329 AVENGING ANGELS £ 420
etching, aquatint and sugar lift
Julia Midgley
(edition of 25: £360 each)

330 APOLLO LOVED DAPHNE £ 900
monotype
Lino Mannocci

331 RIDING THROUGH LAND AND WATER £ 900
monotype
Lino Mannocci

332 EMPIRES Editions available for sale
aquatint
Peter Freeth RA
(edition of 30: £525 each)

333 BALANCE Editions available for sale
aquatint
Peter Freeth RA
(edition of 30: £500 each)

334 AT THE OFFICE £ 160
woodcut
Martin Saull
(edition of 40: £130 each)

335 RESTORATION 2 £ 950
etching
Margaret Sellars

336 UNIVERSE HYPOTHESIS, TORUS £ 160
etching
Theodore Ereira-Guyer
(edition of 40: £130 each)

337 JUST WHAT IS IT THAT MAKES BURGERS SO £ 325
APPEALING, AFTER HAMILTON
woodcut
Gerry Baptist
(edition of 15: £250 each)

338 BERLIN £ 150
etching
Silke Schelenz
(edition of 25: £120 each)

339 PINOCCHIO: TEACHING THE INSECTS
THEIR NUMBERS. 1 £ 160
etching and drypoint
Les Biggs
(edition of 50: £130 each)

340 STUFF £ 115
etching
Martin Langford
(edition of 150: £85 each)

341 SAMARITAN Editions available for sale
aquatint
Peter Freeth RA
(edition of 30: £525 each)

342 FOR YOUR PLEASURE £ 320
etching (hard and soft ground)
Tamsin Relly
(edition of 20: £170 each)

343 TAKAYAMA INTERIOR 2 £ 275
etching with chine collé
Karin Murray
(edition of 6: £225 each)

344 EMPEROR MOTH £ 210
etching
Camilla Clutterbuck
(edition of 10: £160 each)

345 THE APARTMENT (AFTER DELACROIX) I £ 1,760
screenprint
Dexter Dalwood
(edition of 35: £1,200 each)

346 FIREWORKS ON THE THAMES £ 280
wood engraving
John Bryce
(edition of 100: £190 each)

347 SUB (RAMBERT DANCE COMPANY) £ 150
sugar-lift etching
Sally McKay
(edition of 20: £110 each)

348 THE PRINTHOUSE IN HELL £ 260
etching
Oliver McConnie
(edition of 25: £200 each)

349 PEAKSFIELD SUNBURST £ 160
etching
Melvyn Petterson
(edition of 30: £120 each)

350 CITY PAGE 3 Editions available for sale
aquatint
Peter Freeth RA
(edition of 30: £525 each)

351 BODY LANGUAGE £ 370
aquatint
Aimee Birnbaum
(edition of 100: £170 each)

352 SHARD PM £ 1,050
screenprint on graphite
Lucy Bainbridge
(edition of 20: £850 each)

353 OUT OF THE ASHES (I) £ 695
etching and archival digital print
Barton Hargreaves
(edition of 25: £475 each)

354 LIFE IMITATING ART X £ 420
etching and aquatint
Mychael Barratt
(edition of 100: £330 each)

355 ST PAUL'S PM £ 1,050
screenprint on graphite
Lucy Bainbridge
(edition of 20: £850 each)

356 GORMIRE £ 680
etching and aquatint
Jason Hicklin
(edition of 30: £580 each)

357 OAK CHALICE £ 850
aquatint and engraving
Michael Sandle RA
(edition of 30: £680 each)

358 CATAFALQUE £ 850
aquatint and engraving
Michael Sandle RA
(edition of 30: £700 each)

359 PERFECT VARIABLE £ 600
giclée print
Richard Kirwan
(edition of 30: £500 each)

360 KING £ 390
linocut
Martin Langford
(edition of 100: £310 each)

361 A/X £ 350

etching and aquatint
Richard Moon
(edition of 25: £250 each)

362 FARMER'S BRIDGE LOCK, BIRMINGHAM, FAZELEY CANAL £ 230

relief print
Paul Hipkiss
(edition of 25: £190 each)

363 INTERIOR O.C.C £ 280

etching
David Lintine
(edition of 45: £230 each)

364 FANTASMI £ 3,720

etching with leaf (set of 6)
Stephen Chambers RA
(edition of 20: £3,000 each)

365 HOME OF THE GENTRY £ 1,450

screenprint
Stephen Chambers RA
(edition of 30: £1,188 each)

366 THE JOKE AND ITS REACTION £ 1,365

screenprint
Stephen Chambers RA
(edition of 30: £1,135 each)

367 FROM 55 BROADWAY £ 320

etching
Jacqueline Moon
(edition of 10: £250 each)

368 WHITE PARK COW £ 395

stone lithograph
Auberon Hedgecoe
(edition of 12: £325 each)

369 TOUR DE FORCE £ 215

linocut
Lisa Takahashi
(edition of 50: £165 each)

370 PORTAL OF HOPE £ 300
solar plate etching
Handan Sadikoglu
(edition of 25: £220 each)

371 TRIPLE RING I £ 600
etching and aquatint
Julia Farrer
(edition of 7: £550 each)

372 FOLDED £ 395
screenprint on fabriano rosapina
Emma Lawrenson
(edition of 5: £295 each)

373 WINDMILL £ 350
etching with aquatint
Sonia Martin
(edition of 20: £300 each)

374 FROM BLACKFRIARS £ 300
linocut
Peter S. Smith
(edition of 20: £200 each)

375 EVENING RUN £ 450
woodcut
Adrian Bartlett
(edition of 25: £400 each)

376 ON THE WATER £ 500
linocut
Ashley Stark
(edition of 30: £400 each)

377 ST ENODOC £ 350
stone lithography
Simon Burder
(edition of 16: £260 each)

378 ST ENODOC, WIDE £ 350
stone lithography
Simon Burder
(edition of 12: £260 each)

379 RHINOCEROS, IPSWICH MUSEUM £ 190

etching
Derek Chambers
(edition of 26: £150 each)

380 BEAR, IPSWICH MUSEUM £ 190

etching
Derek Chambers
(edition of 26: £150 each)

381 ORCHESTRA III £ 200

linocut
Peter Shread
(edition of 40: £150 each)

382 THOSE LOST FOREVER £ 230

photopolymer and chine collé with pencil
Tammy Mackay
(edition of 30: £145 each)

383 SATOR AREPO £ 350

aquatint etching
Roger Hobdell
(edition of 30: £300 each)

384 MARBLED TWICE SQUARED £ 1,115

copperplate etching
Fianne Stanford
(edition of 10: £700 each)

385 BARN £ 125

giclée print
Rennie Pilgrem
(edition of 100: £95 each)

386 TRANSIENCE IV £ 475

zinc plate lithograph
Sandie M. Henderson
(edition of 3)

387 WORK HORSE £ 460

linocut
Anthony Dyson
(edition of 60: £375 each)

388 COMPOUND £ 2,050

reduction woodcut
Tom Hammick
(edition of 20: £1,750 each)

389 LAST LIGHT, JARDINS DES LUXEMBOURGS, PARIS £ 485

drypoint and monoprint
Lucy Farley
(edition of 20: £365 each)

390 MADONNA £ 350

lithograph and mixed media
Jacki Biddulph
(edition of 30: £300 each)

391 DEGREES OF SEPARATION, A VARIATION £ 350

etching
Francesca Simon
(edition of 10: £300 each)

392 BIRDS IN THE BEAN FLOWERS £ 520

linocut
Anita Klein
(edition of 50: £420 each)

393 REDCAR CASUALS £ 250

linocut and woodblock
Ian Burke
(edition of 25: £180 each)

394 FEATHER AND PEBBLES £ 150

aquatint
Hilary Hanley
(edition of 10: £130 each)

395 AT BAY £ 180

etching
Sarah Rogers
(edition of 70: £140 each)

396 CHESTNUTS £ 120

aquatint
Lawrence Jenkins
(edition of 30: £90 each)

397 FENCE £ 650
woodblock on kozo
Trevor Banthorpe
(edition of 5: £575 each)

398 UNTITLED £ 360
etching
Sharda Mehta
(edition of 50: £320 each)

399 CLOVELLY £ 185
wood engraving
Hilary Paynter
(edition of 200: £140 each)

400 FALSE SECURITY (AFTER JOHN BETJEMAN) £ 345
hand-pulled screenprint
Martin Grover
(edition of 50: £250 each)

401 KING'S RD CALLING £ 425
screenprint
John Butterworth
(edition of 20: £227 each)

402 THE HIGH ST. BALLAD BLUES (AFTER E.R.) £ 420
linoprint
Besheer Abbaro
(edition of 30: £290 each)

403 NIGHT, WESTMINSTER FROM THE £ 2,100
MILLBANK TOWER
monotype
Peter Spens

404 ST PAUL'S AND SHARD, AUGUST 2011 £ 345
etching and aquatint
Austin Cole
(edition of 20: £295 each)

405 WAYFARING: HORSE £ 230
etching
Jane Waterhouse
(edition of 10: £130 each)

406 BORDER MITE II £ 135
etching
Ralph Overill
(edition of 36: £90 each)

407 BORDER MITE III £ 135
etching
Ralph Overill
(edition of 36: £90 each)

408 _ROSE95SOFIA17_ Edions available for sale
hand-pulled black ink on hannemuil paper, drypoint
Katherine Dolgy Ludwig
(edition of 100: £500 each)

409 FIRST HAND £ 235
etching
Alice Llewellyn

410 CUTTY SARK REBORN £ 340
wood engraving
John Bryce
(edition of 100: £250 each)

411 CONDOR CHICK £ 150
monoprint on handmade paper
Diana Poliak

412 BIRD WOMAN £ 220
hand-coloured etching and aquatint
Carolyn Gowdy
(edition of 75: £150 each)

413 REVERSE COZ £ 170
etching
Mark Jones
(edition of 25: £130 each)

414 THE MILLENNIUM BRIDGE AT NIGHT £ 210
linocut
Ben Caro

415 POHUTUKAWA GREEN £ 275
copper etching
Lesley Christiansen
(edition of 15: £150 each)

416 AWAKENING £ 140
acrylic
Emma Caro

417 ALL ARTISTS ARE GOOD ARTISTS £ 500
digital print and screenprint
Mark Hampson
(edition of 40: £400 each)

418 TWELLS' SHED £ 485
drypoint etching
Lindy Norton
(edition of 20: £395 each)

419 RICHMOND NORTH YORKSHIRE HEADS £ 500
linocut and lead type
Sally Cutler
(edition of 50: £450 each)

420 GO FISH, CARD PLAYER DRAWING £ 795
digital, drawing and screenprint
Jenny Wiener

421 PHI £ 300
etching
Niamh Clancy
(edition of 50: £250 each)

422 UROBORO £ 180
etching
Mark Jones
(edition of 20: £140 each)

423 DREAM OF CANALETTO £ 450
etching
Nicholas Richards
(edition of 50: £375 each)

424 HOA BINH (PEACE)   £ 350
etching
Simon Redington
(edition of 50: £275 each)

425 AD1511 – JR2013   £ 870
screenprint
Jolanta Rejs
(edition of 20: £570 each)

426 WATCHFUL R.   £ 1,050
woodcut/monotype
Jolanta Rejs
(edition of 10: £850 each)

427 RAINY NIGHT (THE IVY)   £ 645
etching
John Duffin
(edition of 150: £495 each)

428 SHAMELESS   £ 690
screenprint
Stephen Park
(edition of 35: £540 each)

429 NGUYEN THAI HOC   £ 2,410
woodcut
Christiane Baumgartner
(edition of 16: £1,980 each)

430 DOLOR   £ 9,650
linocut
Richard Galloway

431 THE TUBE, CANARY WHARF   £ 300
etching
Toni Martina
(edition of 75: £240 each)

432 THE TUBE, LONDON   £ 300
etching
Toni Martina
(edition of 75: £240 each)

433 FATHOM 1 £ 420
etching
Jo Gorner
(edition of 30: £350 each)

434 FÉTE £ 490
linocut
Richard Galloway
(edition of 40: £290 each)

435 REMNANT NO. 5 (BY THE BACK DOOR) £1,530
woodcut
Richard Woods
(edition of 40: £1,200 each)

436 (INSERT TITLE HERE) £ 400
digital print
James Bates
(edition of 50: £350 each)

437 TANTRUM CONFESSION £ 1,480
silkscreen with glazes and gilt embossing
Dan Baldwin
(edition of 100: £1,250 each)

438 TOE TO TOE £ 250
linocut and woodblock
Ian Burke
(edition of 25: £180 each)

439 256 COLORS 8BIT £ 750
giclée print, laser cut
Ekkehard Altenburger
(edition of 20: £650 each)

440 LUCIFER £ 570
etching with chine collé
James Fisher
(edition of 20: £480 each)

441 A LEAVING PRESENT, DINOSAUR EGGS £ 395
solar plate etching, chine collé on japanese paper
Marianne Nix
(edition of 30: £295 each)

442 SHALLOW 4 £ 420
etching
Jo Gorner
(edition of 30: £350 each)

443 CIRCLE ETCHING: CADMIUM RED AND DEEP RED £ 2,700
etched monoprint
Ian Davenport

444 BEYOND THE FOREST £ 2,545
woodcut
Lisa Ruyter
(edition of 35: £1,920 each)

445 SOUTH BY SOUTH EAST £ 660
screenprint
Clyde Hopkins
(edition of 75: £480 each)

446 WISH £ 160
solar plate etching
Birgitta Wilson
(edition of 20: £100 each)

447 IN A LONELY PLACE £ 1,500
woodcut
Lisa Ruyter
(edition of 35: £1,200 each)

448 NUDE NOT NAKED £ 1,070
digital print with glazes
Brad Faine
(edition of 50: £850 each)

449 THE GROVE £ 400
giclée print
Alan Patrick Dempsey
(edition of 100: £300 each)

450 GUGGENHEIM BILBAO £ 250
etching
Aileen Jampel
(edition of 25: £200 each)

451 DANDELION £ 120
wood engraving
Penny Mundy
(edition of 10: £90 each)

452 THE GLOBE £ 200
etching
Joseph Winkelman
(edition of 150: £150 each)

453 YORKSHIRE POWER £ 136
etching
Gavin Campbell
(edition of 200: £136 each)

454 STEEL MAKING REDCAR £ 195
etching
David Morris
(edition of 50: £170 each)

455 ELECTRIC AVENUE, A CLOSER LOOK 2 £ 750
sugarlift etching
Simon Lawson
(edition of 20: £550 each)

456 THE BRIDGE £ 650
lithography and screenprint
Philip Davis
(edition of 12: £450 each)

457 LOSS OF INNOCENCE, WAR £ 890
etching and aquatint
Marcelle Hanselaar
(edition of 30: £800 each)

458 THREE-LEGGED RACE, II £ 115
relief print
Sharon Low
(edition of 50: £95 each)

459 SUMMER HOLIDAYS £ 115
relief print
Sharon Low
(edition of 50: £95 each)

460 THE DAILY WALK £ 120
etching
John David Gentry
(edition of 40: £100 each)

461 THE MENDER (DUNGENESS) £ 195
linocut
Andrew Pavitt
(edition of 50: £175 each)

462 LONDON FROM THE EAST, AFTER THE RAIN £ 420
etching
Desmond Healy
(edition of 21: £350 each)

463 ROCKEFELLER CITY £ 495
etching
Neil Pittaway
(edition of 30: £395 each)

464 THE BISHOP'S TOPIARY, ELY £ 150
linocut
A. J. Blustin
(edition of 30: £100 each)

465 RESTING FIGURE £ 180
etching and aquatint
Barbara Herrmann
(edition of 30: £135 each)

466 LA DEA E FECONDO £ 500
etching
Stephen Duncan
(edition of 50: £430 each)

467 IN THE BATH £ 150
wood engraving
Frederick Jones
(edition of 25: £120 each)

468 BENT TREE £ 635
woodcut
Merlyn Chesterman
(edition of 50: £475 each)

469 GUE £ 3,800
monoprint
Marina Brownlow

470 COCKNEY SPARROW £ 500
screenprint
John Bartlett
(edition of 75: £400 each)

471 PROVA £ 420
photopolymer and collograph
Marilène Oliver
(edition of 15: £420 each)

472 INTO THE STORM 2 £ 3,800
monotype
Bill Jacklin RA

473 FALLING LEAVES I £ 3,800
monotype
Bill Jacklin RA

474 CHIRK AQUEDUCT £ 330
etching and aquatint
Jason Hicklin
(edition of 30: £290 each)

475 BLOSSOM WITH BIRD, PART III £ 795
lithograph
Robin Duttson
(edition of 45: £695 each)

476 TAV £ 3,800
monoprint
Marina Brownlow

477 THE GOLDEN ARCHES £ 2,800
48 copperplate etchings printed onto watercolour,
24 carat gold and paper
Bella Easton

478 WALKING AMONGST VESSELS I £ 2,600
collaged printed papers
Charlotte Hodes

479 TRANSITION 2 £ 4,000
monotype
Bill Jacklin RA

480 SETTLED SNOW SIXHILLS £ 380
drypoint
Melvyn Petterson
(edition of 30: £300 each)

481 TUMBLEBEES £ 130
mezzotint and watercolour
Val Mager
(edition of 20: £100 each)

482 CARPUS £ 200
relief print, chine collé
Sharon Lee
(edition of 50: £160 each)

483 WINTER STORM £ 800
etching
Terry Greaves
(edition of 45: £600 each)

484 WALKING AMONGST VESSELS II £ 2,600
printed papers, collaged
Charlotte Hodes

485 FALL £ 680
woodcut
Martin Davidson
(edition of 50: £495 each)

486 ROCK I £ 565
woodcut
Martin Davidson
(edition of 50: £425 each)

487 NOON £ 675
relief etching
Jane Lacy Hodge
(edition of 9: £490 each)

488 DARK WOOD £ 355
woodcut
Sasa Marinkov
(edition of 30: £275 each)

489 THE HURLY BURLY, OXBOW LAKE IN £ 280
FORMATION ON THE RIVER ALN
woodcut
Jonathan Lloyd
(edition of 80: £220 each)

490 ONCE UPON A TIME £ 145
etching
Sarah Garvey
(edition of 75: £95 each)

491 WATERFALL £ 205
aquatint
Ruth de Monchaux
(edition of 40: £135 each)

492 THE THREE RAVENS £ 400
wood engraving
Cathryn Kuhfeld
(edition of 100: £300 each)

493 SEAL MARKET £ 4,200
giclée print
Benjamin Buckley
(edition of 5: £3,800)

494 SLOW SCREAMING #3 £ 1,650
oil-based woodcut
Katsutoshi Yuasa
(edition of 5: £1,400 each)

495 MYTHOLOGY 5 £ 3,870
sugar-lift aquatint with hand-painting
Paul Winstanley
(edition of 5: £3,200 each)

496 THE CATALAN SUITE II, SOUP CAN   £ 1,270
etching
Michael Craig-Martin RA
(edition of 20: £960 each)

497 THE CATALAN SUITE II, SHIRT   £ 1,270
etching
Michael Craig-Martin RA
(edition of 20: £960 each)

498 THE CATALAN SUITE II, PADLOCK   £ 1,270
etching
Michael Craig-Martin RA
(edition of 20: £960 each)

499 MAELSTROM IV   £ 375
aquatint
Marianne Ferm
(edition of 15: £295 each)

500 HOLLYWOOD ROLLERCOASTER   £ 1,000
digital print with glazes
Brad Faine
(edition of 50: £750 each)

501 UNTITLED 1   £ 190
intaglio print
Vera Boele-Keimer
(edition of 7: £140 each)

502 THE BOY AND THE BIRD   £ 380
etching
Davina Jackson
(edition of 100: £185 each)

503 IMPROMPTU   £ 180
etching and wash
Annie Williams
(edition of 40: £130 each)

504 #9 AM OP   £ 1,350
lithograph
Nigel Massey
(edition of 25: £825 each)

505 SWIMMER £ 235
etching and aquatint
Catalina Christensen
(edition of 20: £190 each)

506 BRIDGE TO THE ISLAND ILE DE RÉ £ 395
stone lithograph and watercolour
Lucy Farley
(edition of 15: £255 each)

507 SIGNMAN AND ARIADNE £ 170
etching, drypoint and watercolour
Mike Tingle
(edition of 50: £110 each)

**508 WELCOME TO THE PLEASUREDOME
(465 SUNFLOWERS, 2)** £ 4,500
archival print
Gordon Ellis-Brown
(edition of 100: £4,000 each)

509 STILL LIFE WITH BOUQUET £ 800
inkjet and linocut
Paul Coldwell
(edition of 7: £700 each)

510 STILL LIFE WITH HAIR GRIP AND PAPER CLIP £ 800
inkjet and linocut
Paul Coldwell
(edition of 7: £700 each)

511 TERRACE CORNERS £ 230
relief print
Jeff Clarke
(edition of 20: £200 each)

512 INVERSION £ 285
etching
Susan Gradwell
(edition of 50: £225 each)

513 NEW YORK, EAST SIDE £ 1,200
screenprint, collage and acrylic
Neil Canning

514 CONSTABLE WILLOW £ 420
linocut
Andrew Carter
(edition of 35: £300 each)

515 THE GREAT LONDON PLANE TREE £ 295
aquatint
Mary Cossey
(edition of 100: £250 each)

516 ST PAUL'S AND SHARD, AUGUST 2012 £ 480
etching and aquatint
Austin Cole
(edition of 20: £420 each)

517 SAIL PLAN £ 430
etching
John Roberts
(edition of 40: £390 each)

518 WOODS II £ 265
giclée print
Julia Hutton
(edition of 50: £210 each)

519 IN THE SHALLOWS £ 245
aquatint and etching
Susie Perring
(edition of 120: £185 each)

520 STILL WINTER £ 340
colour woodcut
Josias Figueirido
(edition of 20: £290 each)

521 FOX IN SNOW £ 380
etching
Rachel Levitas
(edition of 36: £320 each)

522 EARLY MORNING (JARDINS DU LUXEMBOURG, PARIS) £ 650
archival inkjet and watercolour print
Jennifer Dickson RA
(edition of 15: £500 each)

523 SPRING RAIN, WALLINGTON GARDEN £ 450
(MECONOPSIS)
archival inkjet and watercolour print
Jennifer Dickson RA
(edition of 15: £350 each)

524 THE MARSH, LANGLEY STREET £ 230
drypoint
Susan Daltry
(edition of 10: £180 each)

525 SEVEN LEMONS £ 800
woodcut
Hilary Daltry
(edition of 50: £650 each)

526 OAK, PINE AND LARCH: WINTER SUNSET £ 415
etching
Piers Browne
(edition of 40: £345 each)

527 THE FOUNTAIN OF THE LIGHTS, VILLA LANTE £ 750
archival inkjet and watercolour print
Jennifer Dickson RA
(edition of 10: £550 each)

528 WATER AND LIGHT (PARQUE DE LA £ 575
CUIDADELA, BARCELONA)
archival inkjet and watercolour print
Jennifer Dickson RA
(edition of 15: £475 each)

529 THE ORGAN FOUNTAIN, VILLA D'ESTE, TIVOLI £ 650
archival inkjet and watercolour print
Jennifer Dickson RA
(edition of 15: £500 each)

530 SPRING AT MILTON LODGE (EUCRYPHIA) £ 450
archival inkjet and watercolour print
Jennifer Dickson RA
(edition of 15: £350 each)

531 ELMS AND WHEATFIELDS, AUTUMN EVENING £ 395
soft-ground etching
Terry Kubecki
(edition of 60: £315 each)

532 CLEMENTINES £ 670
woodcut
Hilary Daltry
(edition of 50: £550 each)

533 DUMB £ 15,000
bronze
Joseph Hillier
(edition of 7: £15,000 each)

534 DREAMCATCHER £ 35,000
lasercut acrylic, ostrich feathers and fishing wire
Marilène Oliver
(edition of 3: £35,000 each)

Large Weston Room

535 HAND (DRAWING FROM THE BRONZE EXHIBITION) £ 1,900
pencil
Stefania Batoeva

536 MOTHER AND CHILD £ 18,000
acrylic
Gerard Hemsworth

537 UNTITLED, 2011 £ 12,500
acrylic on linen
Richard Smith

538 UNTITLED, 2012 £ 12,500
oil
Richard Smith

539 GASTROPODUS £ 4,200
oil on linen
Clyde Hopkins

540 YELLOW HOLZ £ 4,200
acrylic
Christian Junghanns

541 SUDDEN RAIN IN MOMBASA £ 1,400
acrylic
Mohammed Abdullah Ariba Khan

542 WINTER TREES £ 290
linocut
Emma Molony
(edition of 30: £195 each)

543 UNTITLED £ 450
acrylic on linen
Susan Pembridge

544	**SILENCE**	£ 2,000
	acrylic on panel	
	John Renshaw	

545	**AFFLUENZA**	£ 8,000
	polyurethane paint and aluminium panel	
	Ian Daniell	

546	**LA TO LAS VEGAS**	NFS
	acrylic	
	Nick Recordon	

547	**PINES**	£ 180
	ink	
	Valeria Levy	

548	**MISS SIALIA**	£ 1,800
	paper, watercolour, indian ink and shellac	
	Mit Senoj	

549	**HOMAGE TO HOLBEIN**	£ 200
	oil	
	Mary Teresa O'Meara	

550	**STILL LIFE**	£ 1,500
	oil on panel	
	Peter Jones	

551	**SISTER III**	£ 1,800
	indian ink, watercolour and shellac	
	Mit Senoj	

552	**NIGHT LILY**	NFS
	scratchboard	
	Sarah Cloutier	

553	**CRICKET ACADEMY**	NFS
	oil	
	Sagen Zac-Varghese	

554	**A MAN AFTER ILYA REPIN'S OWN HEART**	£ 2,500
	humbrol enamel on board	
	Nathan Eastwood	

555	**COMPOSITION WITH BLACK**	£ 1,500
	watercolour and gouache	
	Stuart Dawson	

556	**MARZAMEMI**	£ 600
	charcoal	
	William Wright	

557	**ALPE D'HUEZ**	NFS
	acrylic	
	Nick Recordon	

558	**LAVENDER SEA II**	£ 480
	acrylic	
	Barbara Cheney	

559	**AJAR**	£ 900
	acrylic	
	Germaine Dolan	

560	**BLACK RADLEY HILL**	£ 850
	mixed media	
	David Cecil Holmes	

561	**FEMALE SPARROW HAWK**	£ 250
	watercolour	
	Katharine Green	

562	**DEEP BLUE SEA, 2012**	£ 330
	cut-out on card	
	Johanna Melvin	
	(edition of 25: £195 each)	

563	**LONG AND SHORT OF IT**	£ 195
	acrylic	
	Jane Broe	

564	**GIRLFIGHT STILL LIFE**	£ 800
	charcoal and pastel on paper	
	Rachel Heller	

565	**TEXT ME YEAH?**	£ 1,500
	acrylic on board	
	Magda Archer	

566 BACK OF BEYOND £ 8,000
acrylic
Paul Tonkin

567 GEMINI £ 950
acrylic
Stephen Jaques

568 YAN SPENCER £ 950
pencil, graphite and watercolour on paper
Cathy Stocker

569 A SMALL PICNIC £ 1,800
acrylic
Luciana Meazza

570 5 COLOUR PAINTING 1 £ 1,875
acrylic on birch plywood panels
Nigel O'Neill

571 TREELINE £ 5,000
oil, acrylic and graphite on aluminium
Ben Ravenscroft

572 5 COLOUR PAINTING 3 £ 1,875
acrylic on birch plywood panels
Nigel O'Neill

573 KNEELING NOT FALLING £ 8,500
oil and acrylic
Lucy Jones

574 LANDSCAPE II £ 1,250
red silk on linen
Miranda Argyle

575 BITTE GEH NICHT FORT £ 1,100
oil on linen
Alberto Torres Hernandez

576 EDGE OF THE KNOWN WORLD £ 3,500
oil on board
Rae Hicks

577 UNTITLED £ 2,500
oil on paper
Rosie Taylor

578 TREIGNAC FIX £ 2,000
gouache and watercolour on paper
Ben Ravenscroft

579 SPRING £ 2,500
acrylic
Tim Allen

580 THE LONG LIST, YOU'RE ON IT TOO! £ 570
acrylic with gloss
Ciplak Gulcehre

581 LIQUID FEVER £ 500
acrylic on wood
Jack Sutherland

582 DANCING CRANES NFS
acrylic on paper
Navnit Mistry

583 UNTITLED 2012 £ 1,600
pencil
Belinda Cadbury

584 HIGGLER £ 3,275
acrylic
Geoffrey Rigden

585 ONWARDS AS THE WORLD SINKS £ 2,600
oil
Geoff Diego Litherland

586 THE HOUSE OPPOSITE £ 15,000
oil
Humphrey Ocean RA

587 LEMON STATIC £ 20,000
oil
Humphrey Ocean RA

588 AMERICAN BOG (1777) NFS
oil
Mark Alexander

589 A CONTEMPORARY LOOK II £ 2,500
oil
Sophie Levi

590 HORSE ON SURFBOARD £ 3,000
oil on board
Harry Hill

591 MUCK £ 1,500
oil on board
Harry Hill

592 GLOBAL VIBRATIONS £ 1,000
oil and pastels
Norman Hayeem

593 LET'S DROP IT, OK? £ 22,000
c–type print mounted on aluminium
Ron Arad RA
(edition of 6: £22,000 each)

594 LET'S DROP IT, OK? SIDEVIEW £ 25,000
c–type print mounted on aluminium
Ron Arad RA
(edition of 6: £25,000 each)

595 MAN ABOUT TOWN £ 108,000
painted mild steel
Allen Jones RA

596 KIRTI £ 2,500
wood
Bartek Arendt, Chris Hill, Eleni Meladaki,
Marina Konstantatou and Yung-Yuan Huang

597 IPSIUS IMAGO A LATERE EXTENSIA £ 42,000
fibreglass painted with acrylics
John Humphreys
(edition of 3: £42,000 each)

598 BLAME THE TOOLS *
*raw stainless steel, mirror polished
stainless steel and bronze rods*
Ron Arad RA

* Refer to Sales Desk

Small Weston Room

599	**NATIVE AMERICAN** *oil* Coral Churchill	£ 1,400
600	**KEITH RICHARDS** *acrylic* Elva Peacock	NFS
601	**SHELLEY, THE SENSITIVE PLANT** *oil* Michael Horovitz	£ 7,500
602	**PAINTING** *oil* Fiona Eastwood	£ 600
603	**PUREMORE** *acrylic* Felix Price	£ 325
604	**ALCYONE** *oil* Nimisha Kotecha	£ 100
605	**MARCH** *charcoal* Stephen Lewis	£ 540
606	**EVENING** *oil* Kim Yahya	£ 11,250
607	**BLONDIE** *acrylic* Angela Rose	£ 385

608 BODIAM CASTLE £ 500
charcoal
Nancy Thomas

609 LOVE £ 1,250
charcoal, pastel
Mulberry Jones

610 RED BIRD £ 900
oil
Charles Harmer

611 MY HEART A WOUNDED CROW £ 750
mezzotint
Sarah Gillespie
(edition of 20: £600 each)

612 PORTRAIT ONE £ 5,000
colour pencil, pastel and watercolour
Yunshu Zhong

613 BENEATH THE EDGE £ 1,500
oil, acrylic and enamel on board
Florin-Catalin Ungureanu

614 THE BEE KEEPERS £ 1,400
oil
Freya Douglas-Morris

615 JCILSCG (JESUS CHRIST IS LORD, £ 1,200
SALTWATER CREEK GARAGE)
acrylic
Steven Wooster

616 KATIE I £ 2,250
oil pastel
Arthur Neal

617 FORMATION 17G £ 280
pencil
Abbi Torrance

618 PILL PACKAGING 2 £ 600
oil on board
Alex Hanna

619 THE DARK SIDE OF THRUSH £ 6,000
oil
Simon W. L. Kilgour

620 BUNCH OF COLOURS £ 300
oil
Korin Nathan

621 BOBBY DRISCOLL (PETER PAN) £ 4,500
oil on paper
Annie Kevans

622 DOT £ 550
mixed media
Maureena Jarvis

623 THE YELLOW SHED £ 1,500
acrylic on board
John Fitzmaurice

624 BUCCANEER £ 450
acrylic
William Vaughan Williams

625 HOLLY (1) £ 925
oil
Roberta Kravitz

626 MY GRANDFATHER, THE PIOUS PATRIARCH NFS
charcoal
Donald Zec

627 ALCHEMIST £ 700
oil on aluminium
Nadine Mahoney

628 HEART'S DESIRES £ 1,200
acrylic
Michael Kennedy

629 NEAR WOOLSFARDSWORTHY £ 4,200
oil on plywood and oak
Hannah Brown

630 UTON 9 £ 4,400
oil on plywood
Hannah Brown

631 FERRIS WHEEL £ 2,000
oil on linen
Nick Carrick

632 THE PRIEST NFS
charcoal
Robert Turrall-Clarke

633 HEAD II £ 2,000
oil pastel
Arthur Neal

634 RETURN OF THE BLUEBLACK HUSSAR £ 15,000
acrylic
Mary Baillie

635 PHOTOFINISHER £ 600
oil on board
Richard McConnell

636 MOVING ON 2 £ 9,500
acrylic and pigments on linen
C. Morey de Morand

637 TWO PICNICS NFS
acrylic, graphite and indian ink on mattress ticking fabric
Phoebe Unwin

638 SIOUX WARRIOR £ 1,400
oil
Coral Churchill

639 CORNWALL SPIRAL £ 50,000
cornish china clay on wood panel
Richard Long RA

640 GIVE OVER £ 2,000
acrylic on board
Magda Archer

641	**CERNUNNOS**	£ 675
	hand stitch on linen	
	Sharon Leahy-Clark	

642	**RURAL SHACK**	£ 800
	oil	
	Matthew Lamb	

643	**INLAND**	£ 260
	screenprint mounted on perspex	
	Hannah Thual	
	(edition of 15: £190 each)	

644	**AROSFA WOODS**	£ 390
	acrylic	
	James Dunkley	

645	**TURF**	£ 1,350
	oil on linen	
	Lucy Boyle	

646	**ROTATOR**	£ 750
	acrylic	
	Stephen Jaques	

647	**LOVE IN THE CITY**	£ 1,500
	acrylic	
	Martina Lanski	

648	**UGO**	£ 1,500
	oil	
	Andrew Seto	

649	**MONDAY OR TUESDAY**	NFS
	soft pastel	
	Angela A'Court	

650	**BACKGROUND II**	£ 1,000
	oil on linen	
	Alex Ball	

661 PC FROM VENICE SAN GIOVANNI IN BRAGORA, VENESSIA £ 35,000
acrylic on canvas on wood relief
Joe Tilson RA

662 PC FROM VENICE SAN PANTALON VENIESIA £ 35,000
acrylic on canvas on wood relief
Joe Tilson RA

663 THE OWL RUN £ 33,600
oil on linen
Hughie O'Donoghue RA

664 DOWN TOWN £ 8,400
acrylic
Albert Irvin RA

665 THE BLACK ROOM (FILTER [BUILDING 2]) £ 3,600
pencil, pen, ink, shellac, pigment, graphite, bronze and copper powder on gesso ground
Benjamin Jenner

666 MR PIKE'S PRIVATE CRAZY GOLF COURSE £ 16,000
ink and pencil on card
Adrian Kidwell

667 MELANCOLIA NFS
woodblock and collage
Anselm Kiefer Hon RA

668 ONE OF THOSE TROUBLESOME 'SINK' HOUSING ESTATES ONE HEARS SO MUCH ABOUT £ 20,000
ink and pencil on card
Adrian Kidwell

669 THE BLACK ROOM (FILTER [BUILDING 1]) £ 3,600
pencil, pen, ink, shellac, pigment, graphite, bronze
and copper powder on gesso ground
Benjamin Jenner

670 YELLOW FLIGHT £ 4,500
acrylic
Maurice Cockrill RA

671 ARISE, THE VERNAL EQUINOX RAM £ 1,500
acrylic
Ron Sims

672 BIRDS II £ 450
mixed media
Britt Frennesson

673 SEAMLESS £ 10,000
oil
Lisa Milroy RA

674 INVISIBLE SHIRT £ 4,000
paper, glue, ink, wood and string
Lisa Milroy RA

675 FIDELIO NFS
acrylic
Albert Irvin RA

676 STRAWBERRY MORNING £ 3,250
acrylic
Ian McKenzie Smith

677 INEXTRICABLY INSEPERABLE £ 285
high relief carborundum print
Leonie King
(edition of 25: £230 each)

678 MUTATIS MUTANDIS XII £ 18,600
acrylic
Paul Huxley RA

679 THE ADOLESCENT £ 1,750
oil
Marguerite Horner

680 ONE MINUTE (42° 49' 02" N. 10° 19' 50" E)   £ 7,200
pencil on tissue
Jessica Arevalo

681 CREEPING SHADOW   £ 1,750
oil
Marguerite Horner

682 ANIMA ANIMUS X   £ 18,600
acrylic
Paul Huxley RA

683 HOLDING MY BREATH   £ 4,500
oil
Janette Kerr

684 UNTITLED (MIES CHAIR)   *
acrylic on aluminium
Michael Craig-Martin RA

685 ORANGE SEED   £ 7,000
acrylic
Maurice Cockrill RA

686 CLEFT   £ 7,000
acrylic
Maurice Cockrill RA

687 EARLY MORNING HAMMERSMITH BRIDGE   £ 12,500
oil
William Bowyer RA

688 SWINGBACK   £ 5,000
acrylic
Mali Morris RA

689 BROKEN GREEN   £ 9,000
acrylic
Maurice Cockrill RA

690 SPROUTING SEED AND YELLOW CLOUD   £ 9,000
acrylic
Maurice Cockrill RA

* Refer to Sales Desk

691 COASTAL PATH £ 3,250
monotype with acrylic, pencil and chalk
Ivor Abrahams RA

692 JOCULAR SPRAWL £ 350
pen and ink
Leonard Manasseh RA

693 WAKE UP £ 350
pen and ink
Leonard Manasseh RA

694 POPPY FUDGE £ 650
pen, ink and gouache
Leonard Manasseh RA

695 DAWN, OR JUST AFTER £ 625
watercolour, pen and ink
Leonard Manasseh RA

696 GIRL IN A BLUE ARMCHAIR £ 3,500
charcoal and pastel
James Butler RA

697 SEA EDGE £ 1,500
monotype with acrylic, pencil and chalk
Ivor Abrahams RA

698 CONFUSED CLARITY £ 650
watercolour, pencil and ink
Leonard Manasseh RA

699 HOSTA £ 8,000
oil
Olwyn Bowey RA

700 WAR ZONE £ 57,000
oil
Maggi Hambling

701 ALEXANDRA £ 18,000
acrylic
Albert Irvin RA

702 WILBURY TWIST *acrylic* Mali Morris RA	£ 5,900
703 WHAT IS THIS, AN ILLUSION! *oil* Philip Sutton RA	£ 13,000
704 MAGIC IN A FACE! *oil* Philip Sutton RA	£ 12,000
705 BONITA'S ANEMONES *oil* Philip Sutton RA	£ 11,500
706 UNTITLED: BROKEN *plywood, cement, plaster, mesh wire netting, paint, scrim, PVA and sand* Phyllida Barlow RA	£ 40,000
707 INEBRIATE OWL *enamel on steel* Ivor Abrahams RA	£ 7,500

708 DRAWING LINES – 4 £ 3,120
mixed media
Ann Christopher RA

709 SENTINEL £ 1,200
monoprint
Phillip King PPRA

710 HIGH SKY £ 1,200
monoprint
Phillip King PPRA

711 DRAWING LINES – 1 £ 3,120
mixed media
Ann Christopher RA

712 DRAWING LINES – 5 £ 3,120
mixed media
Ann Christopher RA

713 PULLED TOOTH DRAWING £ 9,600
reclaimed dental gold drawn into wire and goldplated needle
Cornelia Parker RA

714 PORNOGRAPHIC DRAWING £ 12,000
*ink made from disolving chopped up confiscated
pornographic video tape in solvent, with thanks to
HM Customs and Excise*
Cornelia Parker RA

715 FUSED £ 26,400
cast bronze
Nigel Hall RA
(edition of 6: £26,400 each)

716 ALL THAT REMAINS £ 2,750
concrete and rusty nails on timber canvas
Naomi Doran

717 SILVER LIGHT £ 6,250
pastel
Kenneth Draper RA

718 LIGHT VORTEX £ 6,250
pastel
Kenneth Draper RA

719 QUARRY £ 9,500
mixed media
Jock McFadyen RA

720 A PLACE TO STAY (DIPTYCH) £ 4,000
wood, gesso, archival glue, UV spray, japanese paper
and japanese pigments
Paul Furneaux

721 TRANSITION £ 500
screenprint
John Carter RA
(edition of 40: £400 each)

722 ORANGE £ 1,700
acrylic and wood
John Bremner

723 SUBMERGED WWII BOMBER £ 22,000
watercolour
Michael Sandle RA

724 CATAFALQUE WITH FLARES £ 24,000
watercolour
Michael Sandle RA

725 DEATH ON A TRAIN £ 6,000
ink and wash
Michael Sandle RA

726 DEEP CIRCLES OF LIGHT £ 17,000
mixed media construction
Kenneth Draper RA

727 PREDATOR £ 36,000
foam and pins
David Mach RA

728 PANJAWBHIBAYBI £ 75,000
acrylic
Frank Bowling RA

729 CLOSE £ 72,000
oil
Christopher Le Brun PRA

730 ALL THAT REMAINS £ 35,000
welded aluminium
Jeff Lowe

731 BEYOND THE RIM II £ 22,000
oil and wax
Basil Beattie RA

732 CHRISTSWARM *
wood, GRP, gold leaf and paint
Bill Woodrow RA

733 TOWER £ 58,000
acrylic and charcoal
Tony Bevan RA

734 DRAWING 1620 £ 11,520
acrylic and charcoal
Nigel Hall RA

735 DRAWING 1619 £ 11,520
acrylic and charcoal
Nigel Hall RA

736 SPLIT SHADOW £ 126,000
plaster for bronze
Ann Christopher RA
(edition of 3: £126,000 each)

737 UNO II £ 8,500
fibreglass and epoxy paint
Dhruva Mistry RA

* *Refer to Sales Desk*

738 BIODIVERSITY NEST AT THE EDEN PROJECT   NFS
(WITH BLUE FOREST)
lasercut ply, white card and timber dowel
Jerry Tate Architects

739 COUNTERPOINT   £ 5,600
bronze
Bryan Kneale RA

740 SKY   £ 9,600
stainless steel
Bryan Kneale RA

741 CHALNA, THE GIRL MAILING BY THE POSTBOX   £ 7,000
resin, acrylic and linen on board
Dae Hun Kwon

742 UPDOWN   £ 1,495
wood and metal
Judy Milner

743 TAKING SHAPE NO. 4   £ 2,500
cast iron
Jeff Lowe

744 RUBBERY ENOUGH   £ 2,500
wood
John Cobb

745 RED BRIDGE   £ 1,200
plasterpolymer, pâpier maché, wood, metal,
acrylic paint and varnish
Sadie Brockbank

746 FLOWER   £ 6,000
bronze
Henry Cao

747 PLOVER   £ 12,500
stainless steel
Bryan Kneale RA

748 FLOOD   £ 6,000
deconstructed water-hose
Susie MacMurray

749 KISS £ 7,200
cast bronze on oak base
Nigel Hall RA
(edition of 9: £7,200 each)

750 RIPOLL £ 23,000
forged mild steel
Katherine Gili

VI

751 FRAGMENT £ 300
porcelain, wood and glass
Ikuko Iwamoto
(edition of 40: £300 each)

752 ACROBATICS £ 420
porcelain, wood and glass
Ikuko Iwamoto
(edition of 30: £420 each)

753 BRACING, CHIFLEY SQUARE, SYDNEY NFS
acrylic
Lord Rogers of Riverside RA

754 ART AND DESIGN: 1917 £ 4,700
inkjet print
Michael Craig-Martin RA
(edition of 25: £4,700 each)

755 ARCHITECTONIC FORM 2 £ 1,250
cellulose paint on 3D printed high composite powder and resin
Keith Williams Architects
(edition of 10: £1,250 each)

756 ARCHITECTONIC FORM 1 £ 1,250
cellulose paint on 3D printed high composite powder and resin
Keith Williams Architects
(edition of 10: £1,250 each)

757 ELEVATION STUDIES, DUKE OF YORK STREET/APPLE TREE YARD NFS
timber and timber veneer
Eric Parry RA

758 DANCE WITH ME £ 380
etching and collograph
Antoinette Momtahan
(edition of 10: £315 each)

759 THE MODULAR (DESIGN BY NICK ELDRIDGE,   NFS
MODEL BY STEPHEN SETFORD)
sycamore, perspex and birch ply
Eldridge Smerin

760 A VARIATION ON PIPE DREAMS WITH SWEET   £ 1,950
SWEET BULBS. 3D MINIATURE FRESCO;
A PLASTER RELIEF MOUNTED ON ENGRAVED
PLYWOOD. A NEW EXPRESSION OF THE GARDEN'S
FAÇADE OF OUR PROJECT 'A ROOM FOR LONDON'
(WITH DEE FERRIS, MODEL MAKER: D2W)
plywood and 3D printed plaster
Yael Reisner
(edition of 4: £1,950 each)

761 OPUS 1   £ 500
paper, strings and needles
Giulia Boglietti

762 WAITING TO DANCE   £ 380
etching
Antoinette Momtahan
(edition of 20: £315 each)

763 FAÇADE CONCEPT FOR RESIDENTIAL   NFS
BUILDING ON THE RIVER THAMES
acrylic and MDF model
Stanton Williams

764 SCREEN MEMORY   £ 3,000
pen and ink drawing on board
Wendy Smith

765 KING'S CROSS SQUARE   £ 800
giclée print
Stanton Williams
(edition of 25: £500 each)

766 ACT II: THE FRAGMENTED ROUTE, PLAN   NFS
embossed paper and wire
Eleanor Hedley

767 CHATEAU MARGAUX WINERY, DESIGN   NFS
CONCEPT SKETCHES BY NORMAN FOSTER
pencil
Lord Foster of Thames Bank RA

768 DISPLACEMENT I   £ 600
aquatint
John Carter RA
(edition of 24: £532 each)

769 DISPLACEMENT II   £ 600
aquatint
John Carter RA
(edition of 24: £532 each)

770 UNTITLED (FROM THE 'ECHO OF THE   £ 4,000
SPACE' SERIES)
polished stainless steel
Margarita Trushina

771 TOUCHING THE WORLD LIGHTLY, HILL   NFS
HOUSE (MODEL BY JULIAN PARKER)
patinated mild steel
Martin Williams & Hampson Williams

772 WORCESTER COLLEGE, PERAK   £ 375
etching
Ian Ritchie RA
(edition of 15: £250 each)

773 RSC PEBBLE   £ 375
etching
Ian Ritchie RA
(edition of 15: £250 each)

774 ACT II: THE FRAGMENTED ROUTE   NFS
paper, digital print and wire
Eleanor Hedley

775 EDP FOUNDATION CULTURAL CENTRE   NFS
SLA resin, acrylic paint and MDF base
AL_A

776 THE ENTROPIC GRID OF THE MACHINIST £ 1,950
LANDSCAPE (WITH ED WALL)
linoleum and paper overlay
Mike Dring

---

777 EXPERIMENTAL TOY FACTORY, 02 £ 1,000
pencil
Heechan Park

---

778 SIX DRAWINGS £ 4,000
ink and wash
Bryan Kneale RA

---

779 EXPERIMENTAL TOY FACTORY, 01 £ 1,000
pencil
Heechan Park

---

780 COPENHAGEN LIBRARY COMPETITION, SKETCH £ 250
ink
Paul Koralek RA

---

781 LONDON GARDEN 1 £ 300
ink
Paul Koralek RA

---

782 BRASSICA ONE £ 2,000
ink
Bryan Kneale RA

---

783 VICTORIA AND ALBERT MUSEUM, SKYLINE NFS
watercolour
Daniel Libeskind Hon RA

---

784 BRASSICA TWO £ 2,000
ink
Bryan Kneale RA

---

785 LONDON GARDEN 3 £ 300
pencil
Paul Koralek RA

---

786 DAVENTRY HUB, SKETCH £ 250
pencil
Paul Koralek RA

787 LONDON GARDEN 2 £ 300

pencil
Paul Koralek RA

788 PROJECT IN BELFAST £ 250

pencil
Paul Koralek RA

789 ALGORITHMIC EGG NFS

mixed media
Chris Wilkinson RA

790 INTENSITY, KIND SERIES 1 (TRIPTYCH) £ 1,000

digital print
Felipe Escudero
(edition of 30: £900 each)

791 SOUTHEND PIER HEAD NFS

perspex, SLS plastic, wire and walnut
Price & Myers

**792 SHARJAH WATERFRONT EXPOSITION
HALLS, UAE** NFS

photograph
Sir Michael Hopkins RA

793 PROTOTYPE COVERED BRIDGE NFS

mixed media
Chris Wilkinson RA

794 MUSIC BOX, DETAIL STUDY £ 275

digital print
Darren Furniss
(edition of 25: £200 each)

795 SOMERSET HOUSE: WEST WING NFS

backlit lightbox
Eva Jiricna RA

796 KIND OF BLUE £ 3,000

neon, perspex and wood
Diana Edmunds

797 SOMERSET HOUSE: WEST WING NFS

colour photograph
Eva Jiricna RA

798 GHOSTS OF THE UNDERGROUND £ 250
photographic print
Christopher Drummond
(edition of 20: £120 each)

799 HOUSE MUSIC, DETAIL STUDY £ 275
digital print
Darren Furniss
(edition of 25: £200 each)

800 SOMERSET HOUSE: WEST WING NFS
backlit lightbox
Eva Jiricna RA

**801 WANMU ECOLOGICAL PARK, GUANGZHOU,
CHINA (FLORA)** £ 450
pen, ink and print
Studio 8 Architects
(edition of 5: £400 each)

802 THE NEW LONDON NECROPOLIS, LABYRINTH £ 200
giclée print
Steven Baumann
(edition of 30: £120 each)

**803 SOJDC NO. 4 JERSEY INTERNATIONAL
FINANCE CENTRE, WORKING MODEL
OF FAÇADE BAY 1:50 SCALE** NFS
card
Sir Richard MacCormac RA

**804 BERLIN ARTSPARK (QUADRIPTYCH)
BRASS, CARD AND PAPER FRAMED
RELIEF DRAWINGS** NFS
Mina Gospavić

805 TEXTURE STUDY £ 420
silver gelatin print
Charles K. H. Wu
(edition of 10: £150 each)

806 BERLIN, 1951 £ 1,200
carbon drawing on paper
Chris Shaw Hughes

807 SALIFEROUS MONASTERY, ISTANBUL. £ 900
MONASTERY IN RUIN
pencil, pen, ink and charcoal
Patrick Hamdy
(edition of 20: £750 each)

808 LONDON (VIEW FROM ST PAUL'S), 1941 £ 1,200
carbon drawing on paper
Chris Hughes

809 THE DOVER DICHOTOMY: AERIAL PLAN £ 1,150
matte print
Adam Hiles

810 WANMU ECOLOGICAL PARK, GUANGZHOU, £ 450
CHINA (FAUNA)
pen, ink and print
Studio 8 Architects
(edition of 5: £400 each)

811 MARSEILLE: THE TRANSCENDENTAL PIANO NFS
giclée print
Tom Fotheringham
(edition of 15: £225 each)

812 GOLDEN LADDER HEADS: UP £ 30,000
indian granite (basalt) and gold leaf
Stephen Cox RA

813 HEARTH MEASURES £ 250
pencil and watercolour
Trevor Dannatt RA

814 INUNDATION £ 400
etching
Sir Nicholas Grimshaw PPRA
(edition of 20: £350 each)

815 SET NORTH FOR JAPAN £ 2,000
inflight magazine collage
Richard Wilson RA

816 ARCHITECTURE 2 £ 200
architectural drawing
Laurie Chetwood
(edition of 100: £45 each)

817 BENEATH THE NEW ST JAMES'S PARK £ 950
inkjet print
Ned Scott
(edition of 25: £650 each)

818 MELANCHOLY CIRCUS £ 300
drawing
Yifei Song
(edition of 80: £250 each)

819 THE DOVER DICHOTOMY: £ 1,750
LONGITUDINAL SECTION
matte print
Adam Hiles

820 SEEDS RV £ 300
lithograph on fabriano paper
WeiTao Li
(edition of 15: £200 each)

821 THE MALL £ 950
inkjet print
Ned Scott
(edition of 25: £650 each)

822 THREE-DIMENSIONAL STUDY NFS
FOR BRICKWORK TAKEN FROM
A WORKING DRAWING
inkjet on cartridge paper
Michael Manser RA

823 HOUSE IN 'VILA UTOPIA' NFS
ink on paper
Eduardo Souto Moura

824 VENICE IN THE ROYALS £ 375
etching
Ian Ritchie RA
(edition of 15: £275 each)

825 TAXONOMY OF ALIEN SPECIES £ 500
print and drawing
Peter Hinchliffe
(edition of 20: £400 each)

826 BLUESCAPE I NFS
monoprint
Ian Ritchie RA

827 ELEVATION ON PICCADILLY NFS
(PHOTOGRAPH BY DIRK LINDER)
photographic print
Eric Parry RA

828 MIDWINTER - SPRING £ 950
photographs
Trevor Dannatt RA

829 ARCHITECT LOOKS AT GEORDIELAND, NFS
FOR MAGGIE'S NORTH-EAST
pen
Edward Cullinan RA

830 STUDY FOR AN OFFICE BUILDING NFS
digital print
Lord Rogers of Riverside RA

831 STUDY FOR AN OFFICE BUILDING NFS
digital print
Lord Rogers of Riverside RA

832 PRELIMINARY FAÇADE STUDY, ELEVATION NFS
ON PICCADILLY
pencil and crayon
Eric Parry RA

833 SUNBURST FOR JOHN NFS
monoprint
Ian Ritchie RA

834 BYEONGSANG SEOWON, CONFUCIAN ACADEMY, JOSEON DYNASTY, SOUTH KOREA, 1: 10,000 SCALE (MODEL BY MICHAEL DILLON AND TSUYOSHI WADA)   NFS
plaster cast site model
Michael Dillon

835 DRAWING SHED, BOURNEMOUTH ARTS UNIVERSITY   £ 500
print
Sir Peter Cook RA
(edition of 3: £500 each)

836 DRAWING SHED INTERIOR, BOURNEMOUTH ARTS UNIVERSITY   £ 500
print
Sir Peter Cook RA
(edition of 3: £500 each)

837 DESIGN FOR MANUFACTURE   NFS
acrylic
Lord Rogers of Riverside RA

838 STUDY FOR AN OFFICE BUILDING   NFS
acrylic
Lord Rogers of Riverside RA

839 CHÂTEAU MARGAUX, DESIGN DEVELOPMENT MODELS, ROOF OPTIONS FOR WINERY   NFS
timber foamboard plastic
Lord Foster of Thames Bank RA

840 INTERSECTIONS   £ 2,600
rusted mild steel and glass
Paul Bonomini

841 CHÂTEAU MARGAUX, DESIGN DEVELOPMENT MODELS, BUILDING STUDIES FOR WINERY   NFS
timber foamboard plastic
Lord Foster of Thames Bank RA

842 THINKING IN CIRCLES   £ 800
plaster
Philippa Battye

843 OFFICE BUILDING, CHIFLEY SQUARE, SIDNEY NFS
acrylic
Lord Rogers of Riverside RA

844 SEE LEVEL, DROPWORT RESEARCH CENTRE £ 25
clay
Nichelle Channer

845 METAMORPHOSIS £ 600
wool and plastic bottles
Margaret Barrett

846 GRETNA LANDMARK PROPOSAL NFS
SLA resin prototype model
Chris Wilkinson RA

847 AN ELEMENT OF CORB II £ 3,750
bronze
Philippa Battye

848 MILLENNIUM POINT PAVILION MODEL NFS
1:100, COMPETITION WINNING DESIGN 2013
nylon 3D print and timber base
Daniel Madeiros

849 MEMORY GARDEN FROM 1963 £ 14,000
plastic and aluminium
Phillip King PPRA
(edition of 6: £14,000 each)

850 FURNITURE FOR BOND UNIVERSITY £ 3,000
3D painted wood
Sir Peter Cook RA

851 EINSTEIN MUSEUM JERUSALEM, NFS
DESIGN DEVELOPMENT MODELS
metal, 3D printing, nylon and timber
Spencer de Grey RA

852 SYNTH[E]TECH[E]COLOGY £ 1,000
plywood, acrylic, mesh wire, 3D print and motor
Chang-Yeoh Lee

853 FEAST £ 8,000
plastic food wrap, cotton thread and steel ring
Susie MacMurray

854 TRANSPORT HUB   £ 30,000
paper, stainless steel and plastic
Maj Plemenitas – Linkscale

855 COMPONENT THREE, SERIES TWO   £ 950
walnut and brass
Zoe Fudge

856 BRIDGE AT SLUSSEN, STOCKHOLM   NFS
perspex
Spencer de Grey RA

857 TEESSIDE POWER STATION   NFS
3D print SLS, bronze, perspex and wood
Heatherwick Studio

858 FITZROVIA COMPOSITION STUDY II   NFS
timber veneer
DSDHA

859 A SENSE OF PLACE   NFS
model
Studio Egret West

860 HELSINKI LIBRARY (MODEL BY 'A MODELS')   NFS
plywood, perspex and metal
Giles Reid Architects

861 CONCEPT MODELS FOR THE   £ 6,000
FESTIVAL WING, SOUTHBANK CENTRE
(MODEL BY KEN GRIX)
cast concrete and perspex
Feilden Clegg Bradley Studios

862 ROYAL ACADEMY OF ARTS BRIDGE   NFS
foam core and cardboard
Sir David Chipperfield RA

863 BREWESTER HOUSE, HIGHGATE   NFS
(WOOD MODEL BY PIPERS AND
PLASTIC MODEL BY JOHN COOK)
plastic and wood
Birds Portchmouth Russum Architects

864 LHA LONDON, TORQUAY HOUSE,   NFS
PRESENTATION MODEL 1:200 SCALE
(MODEL BY EVA POSPECHOVA)
white card
MJP Architects

---

865 SOMERSET HOUSE: WEST WING   NFS
model
Eva Jiricna RA

---

866 HACKNEY BRIDGE   NFS
model
Amin Taha Architects

---

867 GARDEN MUSEUM, 1:200 SCALE   NFS
CONCEPT MODEL
wood, acrylic, copper, cardboard, sandpaper, plaster and MDF
Dow Jones Architects

---

868 SOMERSET HOUSE: WEST WING   NFS
(MANUFACTURER: IL CANTIERE,
STRUCTURAL ENGINEER: TECHNIKER)
prototype tread, concrete and stainless steel
Eva Jiricna RA

---

869 MASDAR MOSQUE   NFS
3D print ABS, perspex, wood, paper, brass and fibre optics
Heatherwick Studio

---

870 RSC PEBBLE CONCEPT MODEL   £ 2,000
painted cast resin
Ian Ritchie RA

---

871 CONCEPT MODEL FOR STUDENT   NFS
RESIDENTIAL BUILDING AT KING'S CROSS
walnut, acrylic and MDF model
Stanton Williams

---

872 FIGURE TURNING: AFTER YOUTH OF MOTYA   £ 70,000
egyptian alabaster with pencil
Stephen Cox RA

---

873 CHINESE BIOME PROJECT   NFS
wood and plastic
Sir Nicholas Grimshaw PPRA

874 WESTMINSTER PLACE NFS
wood, acrylic and metal
Allford Hall Monaghan Morris

875 LOOM, TEMPORARY PAVILION FOR PREFAB £ 8,500
EVENT SERIES, LONDON (MODEL BY
BRIAN MACKEN WITH FACTORY ARCHITECTURE)
fabric, acrylic and timber
Factory Architecture

876 THE JERUSALEM BRAIN SCIENCES NFS
BUILDING, DESIGN DEVELOPMENT MODELS
timber and perspex
Spencer de Grey RA

877 SHAFTESBURY THEATRE, LONDON NFS
cardboard, timber and resin
Bennetts Associates Architects

878 GREAT WHITE £ 15,000
wood, plaster, paint and appropriated objects
Tony Carter

879	**DISPLACED** *oil and paper on board* Trevor Sutton	£ 7,000
880	**SUB SERIES #8** *acrylic and collage on paper* Alison Wilding RA	£ 1,800
881	**SUBS SERIES #7** *acrylic and collage on paper* Alison Wilding RA	£ 1,800
882	**HOLYBOURNE** *acrylic* Will Alsop RA	£ 17,500
883	**MEDLEY** *mixed media* Philippa Stjernsward	£ 6,500
884	**FOUR ROWS** *acrylic* Stephen Webster	£ 1,800
885	**ABSAGEWEISSE** *oil on linen and acrylic* Jane Bustin	£ 7,000
886	**CLIMBING BEACON** *collagraph on paper* Katherine Jones (edition of 25: £600 each)	£ 750
887	**FLORENCE** *oil and acrylic* Alexander Vorobyev	£ 15,000

888	**FLIRT**	£ 9,000
	oil	
	Jane Harris	
889	**COPPER SPIRES III**	£ 3,000
	oil and ink on handmade paper	
	Barbara Macfarlane	
890	**UNSTUCK IN TIME**	£ 6,500
	acrylic	
	John Wragg RA	
891	**ELECTRIC DREAM**	£ 5,250
	acrylic	
	John Wragg RA	
892	**FIRST DANCE**	£ 6,500
	acrylic	
	John Wragg RA	
893	**LAST CALL**	£ 8,500
	acrylic	
	John Wragg RA	
894	**SISTER OF DREAMS**	£ 8,500
	acrylic	
	John Wragg RA	
895	**TORSO 1**	£ 12,000
	graphite and watercolour	
	David Remfry RA	
896	**TORSO 2**	£ 12,000
	graphite and watercolour	
	David Remfry RA	
897	**THE SORROWS OF YOUNG OSCAR**	£ 15,000
	graphite and watercolour	
	David Remfry RA	
898	**PORTRAIT OF CAREL WEIGHT**	NFS
	pencil, pastel, watercolour and gold leaf	
	Leonard McComb RA	

899 PORTRAIT OF REBECCA £ 40,000
pencil and pastel with traces of gold leaf
Leonard McComb RA

900 SLOW TURN £ 6,250
graphite and watercolour
David Remfry RA

901 #1 FROM THE RUNAWAYS SERIES £ 200
mixed media on found button
Hannah Battershell

902 MAGENTA ON BLACK £ 160
ink on acrylic
Gay Halley

903 #1 – II £ 3,000
graphite
Gary Edwards

904 TEMPORAL DISLOCATION 002 £ 1,755
(CONCRETE FOUNDATION)
lambda c-type photograph mounted on aluminium
James Smith
(edition of 5: £1,170 each)

905 MAPPA MUNDI PARIS £ 900
thermal ribbon transfer on vinyl
Ewan David Eason
(edition of 100: £750 each)

906 STRUCTURAL ABSTRACT £ 5,500
acrylic
Chris Wilkinson RA

907 TEMPORAL DISLOCATION 007 (HAYSTACK) £ 1,755
lambda c-type photograph mounted on aluminium
James Smith
(edition of 5: £1,170 each)

908 DAY OF GRACE £ 3,000
handmade paper and acrylic
Sheila Girling

909 INTERNAL AND EXTERNAL 1 £ 12,000
ink, acrylic and oil pastel
Gordon Benson RA

910 ACOUSTIC SCORE 1 £ 9,000
ink, acrylic and oil pastel
Gordon Benson RA

911 UNTITLED 1 £ 15,000
ink, acrylic and oil pastel
Gordon Benson RA

912 INTERNAL AND EXTERNAL 2 £ 12,000
ink, acrylic and oil pastel
Gordon Benson RA

913 ACOUSTIC SCORE 2 £ 9,000
ink, acrylic and oil pastel
Gordon Benson RA

914 INTERNAL AND EXTERNAL 3 £ 12,000
ink, acrylic and oil pastel
Gordon Benson RA

915 DAY BY DAY £ 3,000
handmade paper and acrylic
Sheila Girling

916 MUSEO JUMEX MODEL 2 NFS
mixed media
Sir David Chipperfield RA

917 TWENTY TRIANGLES £ 6,950
pressed and welded cartridge brass
Richard Grimes

918 COLNEY COLUMN £ 75,000
fibreglass with acrylic paint
Ivor Abrahams RA

919 DOCKET IN MY HAND £ 1,800
bronze with silver nitrate patina
Tracey Emin RA
(edition of 100: £1,800 each)

920 CHAOS £ 3,550
bronze
Mark Yale Harris

921 ORANGE SURF £ 12,000
foam and pins
David Mach RA

922 LOS DOS OMBRES £ 36,000
foam and pins
David Mach RA

923 MING £ 28,000
foam and pins
David Mach RA

924 BRITTEN-PEARS ARCHIVE, ALDEBURGH NFS
birch plywood and copper
Stanton Williams

925 NIKE £ 17,000
silver-plated bronze
James Butler RA
(edition of 6: £17,000 each)

926 HOUSE OR SCULPTURE? (DESIGN BY NFS
NICK ELDRIDGE AND MODEL BY DETAIL)
cor-ten steel and stainless steel
Eldridge Smerin

927 NEMEAN REFRACTION £ 3,500
bronze and granite
Mark Atkins
(edition of 14: £3,500 each)

928 STUDY MODEL FOR A BUILDING ADJUSTED NFS
TO MULTIPLE PLACES AND SCALES
mixed media
Jonathan Houser

929 SITTING BULL £ 8,500
fibreglass and epoxy paint
Dhruva Mistry RA

930 JASPER NFS
archival watercolour pigment print (90°)
Chuck Close
(edition of 3)

931 ADA 2 *
oil on linen
Alex Katz

932 PORTRAIT OF J. D. £ 7,800
oil on linen
Stephen Chambers RA

933 PORTRAIT OF S. W. £ 7,500
oil on linen
Stephen Chambers RA

934 ME AND ME £ 72,000
silver gelatin print
Marina Abramovic Hon RA
(edition of 9: £72,000 each)

935 NEAMA EL SAYED AND HER CHILDREN, £ 168,000
WHOSE FATHER, LOTFY AZZAM, WAS
KILLED BY A SNIPER DURING THE PROTESTS
gloss on aluminium
Gary Hume RA

936 MARIA TERESA 1 £ 42,000
inkjet on canvas
Julian Opie

937 SAM NFS
gouache
Humphrey Ocean RA

* *Refer to Sales Desk*

938 ZELIE
gouache
Humphrey Ocean RA

NFS

---

939 GARDEN BOY
oil
Mark Alexander

£ 45,000

---

940 TRANSIT DISASTER GAS MASK SILVER PORTRAIT
silkscreen ink on canvas
Gavin Turk

£ 45,600

---

941 BETULA PENDULA 'FASTIGIATA' (SOUS-CHEF ON SMOKE-BREAK)
painted aluminium lightbox with transmounted chromogenic transparency
Rodney Graham
(edition of 5)

£ 195,000

---

942 PARK DE LA CUIDADELA, BARCELONA, JUNE 4, 2005
inkjet print
Rineke Dijkstra
(edition of 10)

NFS

---

943 COMMISSIONED PORTRAIT UNTITLED (GILLIAN)
wall-mounted LCD monitor computer with integrated software
Michael Craig-Martin RA

*

---

944 SELF-PORTRAIT
acrylic and charcoal
Tony Bevan RA

£ 38,400

---

945 I THOUGHT SHE WASN'T LOOKING
acrylic
John Wragg RA

£ 5,250

---

946 KATE ENCASED
oil on canvas with shelf
Allen Jones RA

NFS

---

947 UNTITLED
oil
Anne Ryan

£ 7,200

* Refer to Sales Desk

948 ANNELA £ 20,000
oil
Celia Paul

949 YOKO XII Editions are available for sale
inkjet print
Don Brown
(edition of 5: £10,135 each)

950 M.C. NFS
watercolour
Elizabeth Peyton

951 PORTRAIT OF WILLIAM FEAVER NFS
graphite and chalk
Frank Auerbach

952 MARGOT + FERGUS, 11 NOVEMBER 2008 NFS
coloured pencil
Elizabeth Peyton

953 SELF-PORTRAIT: TRIPLEGÄNGER £ 8,000
oil and collage
Tom Phillips RA

954 INFORMERS (DIPTYCH) £ 1,800
oil on gessoed panel
Sarah Ball

955 CONSPIRATORS (DIPTYCH) £ 1,800
oil on gessoed panel
Sarah Ball

956 SELF-PORTRAIT IN THE YEAR 2087 *
bronze, gold leaf and paint
Bill Woodrow RA

957 PORTRAIT OF LORD DEAR £ 15,000
bronze
James Butler RA
(edition of 3: £15,000 each)

* Refer to Sales Desk

958 WOMAN IN RED £ 870
archival digital print
Guler Ates
(edition of 10: £590 each)

959 ETERNAL MAHARANA AND SHE (I) £ 1,400
archival digital print
Guler Ates
(edition of 10: £950 each)

960 LOVE IN VITEBSK £ 400
photograph
David Olsan
(edition of 300: £300 each)

961 THE LONG WAIT (FROM THE SERIES £ 15,700
BORDER, 2005-2006)
c-print with diasec mount
Mitra Tabrizian
(edition of 5)

962 ST DOROTHY £ 1,900
c-type hand print
Liane Lang
(edition of 3: £1,600 each)

963 BASE CAMP £ 780
c-print on aluminium
Martin Bardell
(edition of 5: £560 each)

964 URSULA WITH VIRGINS £ 3,200
durst lamda print
Liane Lang
(edition of 3: £2,700 each)

965	**TEENS IN WAITING ROOM, HEADS DOWN**	£ 3,420
	photograph	
	David Stewart	
	(edition of 5: £2,850 each)	

966	**MEGALOMANIAC**	£ 4,800
	framed colour photograph mounted on aluminum	
	Petros Chrisostomou	
	(edition of 3: £4,500 each)	

967	**VOID**	£ 660
	photography	
	Alicia González-Lafita Pérez	
	(edition of 5: £540 each)	

968	**IN NORAS SHADOW**	£ 1,300
	acrylic ink on sheet metal	
	Catherine Barron	

969	**A MODERN HALLUCINATION**	£ 850
	c-type photographic print	
	Juno Calypso	
	(edition of 5: £650 each)	

970	**RECOMBINANT 1**	£ 350
	120mm photograph	
	Joseph Thomas	
	(edition of 10: £300 each)	

971	**LA NIÑA, EL NIÑO**	£ 450
	collage	
	Caroline Kha	

972	**SIXTH AVENUE**	£ 950
	screenprint	
	John Mackechnie	
	(edition of 25: £800 each)	

973	**FIELD EDGE 10**	£ 2,250
	acrylic on board	
	Vanessa Gardiner	

(handwritten: 974 circled) *Sam.*

974 TRAIGH £ 950
screenprint
John Mackechnie
(edition of 25: £800 each)

975 CLIFF WALL 7 £ 2,500
acrylic on board
Vanessa Gardiner

976 DIPPER £ 400
archival digital print
Miyako Narita
(edition of 20: £300 each)

977 FRENCH SHRIMPERS 1 £ 950
giclée photographic print
Joel Redman
(edition of 20: £575 each)

978 WELLS NV £ 5,500
archival pigment transfer print
Boyd & Evans
(edition of 10: £4,750 each)

979 DELUGE NM £ 8,800
archival pigment transfer print
Boyd & Evans
(edition of 10: £7,500 each)

980 UNDERCURRENT £ 1,250
inkjet photograph
Jean Macalpine
(edition of 10: £1,150 each)

981 SHIPWRECK £ 1,875
archival inkjet print
Peter Gudynas
(edition of 25: £1,775 each)

982 FRENCH SHRIMPERS 2 £ 950
giclée photographic print
Joel Redman
(edition of 20: £575 each)

983 SOCAR OIL FIELDS #3, BAKU, AZERBAIJAN   £ 14,000
photograph
Edward Burtynsky
(edition of 9: £13,500 each)

984 THE TOWER   £ 750
photograph
Mike Harding
(edition of 10: £600 each)

985 THE CAGE   £ 750
photograph
Mike Harding
(edition of 10: £600 each)

986 WINTER 22   £ 6,600
digital print laminated to glass
Julian Opie
(edition of 3: £6,600 each)

987 TREE IN THE MIST   £ 2,200
pigment print on diasel
Tim Hall
(edition of 12: £1,600 each)

988 REYKANESBRAUT   £ 510
etching
Bronwen Sleigh
(edition of 20: £400 each)

989 LARGE TURF, 2013 (FROM MODEL SERIES)   £ 1,900
graphite frottage and pencil on paper
Jane Dixon

990 CAST, 2011 (FROM MODEL SERIES)   £ 1,900
graphite frottage and pencil on paper
Jane Dixon

**991 UNTITLED (FROM THE SERIES
'BLURRED TIMES')**   £ 1,950
photograph
Virgilio Ferreira

992 WATER PAINTING £ 450
film
Susie David
(edition of 5: £450 each)

993 CAR COMPASS £ 8,000
film
Eye Try
(edition of 3: £8,000 each)

994 CIRQUE SIVRAJ NFS
film
Roland Jarvis

995 SIMULATED WARFARE £ 300
film
Oliver Parkin

996 MEMORIAL 2 £ 780
silver gelatin print
Peter Gibbons

997 AIRLINE FOOD (A SCANNING ELECTRON £ 1,000
MICROGRAPH OF DISOLVED SALT
REPRESENTING THE 30% EXTRA SALT
NEEDED FOR FOOD TO TASTE THE SAME UP
IN THE AIR AS IT DOES ON GROUND)
sem photograph, digital print
Signe Emma
(edition of 7: £900 each)

998 THE CREATION OF ARDUINUM £ 15,000
digital photo print
Lucas Tizard
(edition of 11: £12,500 each)

999 CURVED WALL, SQUARE WINDOW £ 80
photograph
Celia May Strainge
(edition of 30: £25 each)

1000 UNTITLED £ 80
photographic print
Garey Lennox
(edition of 20: £50 each)

1001	**RIO. CITY PATTERN**	£ 350
	giclée print	
	Mike Leale	
	(edition of 25: £250 each)	

1002	**NO. 28**	£ 2,500
	platinum baryta paper print	
	Adam Sillito	
	(edition of 12: £2,000 each)	

1003	**BRIGHTON CAROUSEL**	£ 450
	photograph on hand-coloured paper	
	Janine Kilroe	

1004	**PAINTING HIS OWN SHADOW**	£ 840
	c-type print	
	Christopher Jonas	
	(edition of 10: £600 each)	

1005	**ST JAMES'S PARK**	£ 850
	giclée print	
	Changwoo Ryu	
	(edition of 7: £750 each)	

1006	**LONDON, BEYOND THE WINDOW**	NFS
	digital print on metal	
	Daniela Rizzo	

1007	**HELICONIA**	£ 260
	photogravure	
	Norman McBeath	
	(edition of 30: £200 each)	

1008	**DUST ACCUMULATION (+7 YEARS)**	£ 300
	c-type print on archival paper	
	Heather Miller	
	(edition of 50: £250 each)	

1009	**PERISHING #1**	Editions available for sale
	gelatin silver photographic print	
	Caroline Silverwood Taylor	
	(edition of 10: £700 each)	

1010 TWENTY ONE £ 987

ambrotype: collodion positive
Jacqueline Macrae

1011 WAITING £ 7,500

c-type photographic print from negative
Scott Mead
(edition of 5: £6,000 each)

1012 ARTIST'S HOUSE, TOKOMARU BAY £ 7,200

c-type photographic print
Bridget Smith
(edition of 3: £7,200 each)

1013 ANON (GIRL) £ 255

photograph
Louisa Holecz

1014 ANON (BOY) £ 255

photograph
Louisa Holecz

1015 UNTITLED: XINJIANG, CHINA £ 750

photographic print on aluminium
David Thurston
(edition of 12: £750 each)

1016 HELLUR £ 425

photograph
Tina Vanderwerf
(edition of 8: £425 each)

1017 HARMONICA £ 955

mezzotint
Marie Harnett
(edition of 35: £810 each)

1018 BRILLO £ 955

mezzotint
Marie Harnett
(edition of 35: £810 each)

1019 FRED   £ 1,600

c-type print
Jooney Woodward
(edition of 5: £1,400 each)

1020 QUAIL   £ 400

c-type print
Miyako Narita
(edition of 20: £300 each)

1021 SPACE COAST   £ 500

photograph
David Ryle
(edition of 20: £350 each)

1022 HAND ME DOWN A CLASSIC   £ 360

screenprint
Claire Robinson
(edition of 10: £280 each)

1023 THE HEALER   £ 700

giclée print, neodymium magnets and iron filings
Roberto Ekholm
(edition of 50: £500 each)

1024 FRICTION 5   £ 1,200

archival print
Phil Shaw
(edition of 60: £1,125 each)

1025 ST PAUL'S   £ 375

photograph
Adrian Ensor
(edition of 25: £300 each)

1026 PORTLAND PLACE   £ 375

photograph
Adrian Ensor
(edition of 25: £300 each)

1027 GRAND TOUR: IN SEARCH OF SOANE   £ 9,800
(AFTER GANDY)

transparency on LED lightbox
Emily Allchurch
(edition of 15: £9,800 each)

1028	**KALK BAY HARBOUR**	£ 590
	screenprint of 35mm negative	
	Vita Hewison	
	(edition of 5: £440 each)	

1029	**LAGUNE 1**	£ 340
	photograph	
	Olivier Durrande	
	(edition of 10: £340 each)	

1030	**UNTITLED**	£ 295
	giclée print	
	Jon-Paul Davis	
	(edition of 50: £195 each)	

1031	**HOUSE #3**	£ 650
	photograph	
	Mandy Williams	
	(edition of 5: £380 each)	

1032	**CHURCH OF ST VLADIMIR, 1757, PODPOROZHYE**	£ 1,100
	inkjet print	
	Richard Davies	
	(edition of 25: £950 each)	

1033	**CHURCH OF ST MICHAEL, 1655,** KRASNAYA LYAGA	£ 1,100
	inkjet print	
	Richard Davies	
	(edition of 25: £950 each)	

1034	**MUNICH**	£ 450
	colour print	
	Elke Bock	
	(edition of 25: £250 each)	

1035	**WEST PIER, HOVE**	£ 120
	silver gelatin print	
	Wayne Foskett	
	(edition of 50: £110 each)	

1036	**THAMES AT CHARLTON**	£ 120
	silver gelatin print	
	Wayne Foskett	
	(edition of 50: £110 each)	

1037	**STRIPPED NO. 1**	£ 650
	photograph	
	Brian Rybolt	
	(edition of 125: £450 each)	

1038	**FINAL DELIVERY**	£ 225
	photograph	
	Darren Nisbett	
	(edition of 10: £185 each)	

1039	**DRIFTWOOD**	£ 225
	photograph	
	Darren Nisbett	
	(edition of 10: £185 each)	

1040	**GENERATOR ROOM**	£ 360
	photogravure	
	Norman McBeath	
	(edition of 30: £275 each)	

1041	**HANGING MOUNTAIN**	NFS
	pencil, graphite and paint on paper	
	Laura Kelly	

1042	**FRANCOISE**	£ 900
	glass negative, collage and paint	
	Mollie Tearne	

1043	**VINCENT**	£ 900
	glass negative, collage and paint	
	Mollie Tearne	

1044	**BAYOU**	£ 730
	giclée print on enhanced matte paper	
	Suzanne Moxhay	
	(edition of 10: £575 each)	

1045 EYRIE £ 825
giclée print on enhanced matte paper
Suzanne Moxhay
(edition of 10: £625 each)

1046 BARLEY BY THE DON £ 2,000
acrylic gum bichromate print
Terry King

1047 DIABAIG £ 115
etching
Sarah Granville
(edition of 25: £85 each)

1048 TERRA INCOGNITA #01 £ 995
photograph
Andrea Morley

1049 MATLEY WOOD £ 2,995
archival pigment print, diasec
Shinwook Kim
(edition of 7: £600 each)

1050 05:57 NOTHING TO DECLARE £ 2,900
oil on card mounted on panel
Ben McLaughlin

1051 NOTES SERIES, NO 35 [ONE OF A SERIES £ 500
OF EXPLORATIONS PRESENTING A SUBLIME
LANDSCAPE AS AN IDEA OR A CERTAIN
STATE OF MIND; AN AMBIGUOUS PLACE OF
TRANSITION IN BETWEEN THOUGHTS]
mixed media, paint and graphite on board
Sue Williams A'Court

1052 SUMMER OF 2012 £ 4,000
newspaper, kakishibu, sumi ink and paints
Yoshimi Kihara

Lecture Room

1053	**ST PAUL'S, WITH REFLECTION** *pastel* Anthony Eyton RA	£ 7,500
1054	**SELF-PORTRAIT** *oil* William Bowyer RA	£ 8,000
1055	**THE STONEMASON, MARRAKECH** *acrylic* Ian Hargreaves	£ 1,600
1056	**END OF EMPIRE IN THE BRITISH MUSEUM** *oil on paper* Georgia Hayes	£ 7,500
1057	**TEDDY AND TULIPS** *oil on paper* Mary Barnes	£ 495
1058	**THE SPACE BETWEEN HEARTBEATS** *oil* Eric Seeley	£ 3,250
1059	**GRAPEVINES (LOWER AUSTRIA)** *oil* Anne-Marie Oshelda	£ 800
1060	**CALM BEFORE THE STORM** *oil on board* Marisa Willoughby-Holland	£ 1,750
1061	**THE GARDENS IN JANUARY** *oil on panel* Glyn Saunders	£ 750

| 1062 | **CORNISH MEMORIES** | £ 2,500 |

oil
Martin Leman

| 1063 | **KEYS** | £ 4,850 |

oil on panel
Robbie Wraith

| 1064 | **A HEAD FULL OF PICTURES** | £ 16,800 |

oil
Anthony Green RA

| 1065 | **LIVERPOOL STREET STATION CONCOURSE 2** | £ 6,000 |

pastel
Anthony Eyton RA

| 1066 | **PEACH FUZZ** | £ 800 |

oil on linen
Lisa Smithey

| 1067 | **YESTERYEAR** | £ 3,500 |

oil
Derek Ellwood

| 1068 | **THE PERFORMER** | £ 800 |

gouache
Bridget Moore

| 1069 | **SNOWDONIA** | £ 3,950 |

egg tempera on gesso board
Andrew George

| 1070 | **THE ARTIST'S DOG** | £ 650 |

acrylic
Louise Waugh

| 1071 | **OLIVES** | £ 850 |

oil
Michael Tarr

| 1072 | **TIMESPAN** | £ 12,000 |

oil
Carey Clarke

1073	**XXXX, 1.6**	£ 4,765
	mono lithographic process	
	Emma McGuire	
	(edition of 3: £4,000 each)	
1074	**THE LATTE DRINKER**	£ 300
	mixed media	
	Jane Cornford	
1075	**ENIDS CAT**	£ 2,400
	oil on board	
	Susan Bower	
1076	**BORROWED FLOWERS WITH IMAGINARY VASE**	£ 4,500
	acrylic and photographic ink	
	Michael Esk	
1077	**BRENDAN QUICK**	£ 700
	enamel on aluminium	
	Geraldine Swayne	
1078	**STILL LOOKING BACK AT ME LOOKING BACK**	£ 1,500
	oil and gesso on paper	
	Susie Hunt	
1079	**PLAY**	£ 1,400
	oil and pencil on board	
	Teresa Lawler	
1080	**THE WIND**	£ 2,500
	oil	
	Saul Robertson	
1081	**JERUSALEM 2005**	£ 35,000
	oil	
	John Bellany RA	
1082	**OUTSIDE THE ROMA CAFÉ**	£ 4,000
	oil	
	Simon Quadrat	
1083	**ARRIERE PENSÉE**	£ 6,850
	oil on panel	
	Robbie Wraith	

1084 NIGHT FLIGHTS   £ 18,000
watercolour and graphite
David Remfry RA

1085 ICE FISHING   £ 1,850
acrylic on wood
Nicola Slattery

1086 SERPENT AND CITY   £ 1,120
oil
Paul Saari

1087 DAY-DREAMS!   £ 18,500
oil
Philip Sutton RA

1088 IT'S JUST A GAME   £ 10,000
oil
Xiaocen Liu

1089 THE GIRL WITH AUBURN HAIR   £ 1,200
oil
June Berry

1090 UNTITLED I   £ 1,200
oil
Julian Gordon Mitchell

1091 THE RED BERET   £ 95
mixed media
Lesley Birch

1092 TEACUPS IN THE FINANCIAL TIMES   £ 17,000
oil
Benjamin Hope

1093 WINTER   £ 2,500
mixed media
Henry Kondracki

1094 EXHIBIT V   £ 450
acrylic on décollage
Simon Kirk

1095 THE REMAINS £ 1,300
acrylic ink on sheet metal
Catherine Barron

1096 APRIL SHOWERS £ 4,000
oil on panel
Alex Maw

1097 LOOKING SOUTH WEST FROM BRANDON HILL, BRISTOL, PLEIN AIR £ 500
oil on board
Tom Hughes

1098 MILLENNIUM BRIDGE £ 900
oil
Craig Sumner

1099 LEVIATHAN £ 1,400
oil
Paul Saari

1100 A BETTER DAY £ 850
acrylic
Paul Gadenne

1101 ABNEY PARK BY MOONLIGHT £ 12,000
oil
Emma Haworth

1102 TITANIA £ 13,500
oil
Miriam Escofet

1103 THE 1970 WORLD ALMANAC AND BOOK OF FACTS £ 2,800
balsa wood, paper and acrylic paint
Sarah Bridgland

1104 A MODERN OLYMPIA VIII £ 12,000
oil
Anthony Green RA

1105 A MODERN OLYMPIA (TOY BOY) IX £ 14,400
oil
Anthony Green RA

1106 RED UNDERWING MOTH, CATOCALA NUPTA £ 300
pencil and blackboard paint on antiquarian book cover
Helen Hunt

1107 CALLUM £ 2,200
oil
Louis Turpin

1108 DRAWING CLASS £ 1,250
oil
Michael Kirkbride

1109 FLOWERS £ 40,000
oil
John Bellany RA

1110 TO END ALL WARS £ 1,800
acrylic
Joan Hickson

1111 A MODERN OLYMPIA IV £ 19,200
(AG LOVES MARY VERY VERY MUCH)
oil
Anthony Green RA

1112 BLUE MEMORIES/LONDON £ 16,800
oil
Anthony Green RA

1113 CONFUSION CAN BE A USEFUL CONDITION £ 4,250
acrylic
David L. Carpanini

1114 WHITE SLUICE GATE £ 900
pigment and acrylic
David Brayne

1115 LONDON CITYSCAPE, ST PAUL'S, £ 9,850
MORNING SUN
oil on board
Robert John Shaw

1116 IN THE GARDEN £ 10,000
oil and acrylic
Alexander Vorobyev

1117 WOMAN IN PINK £ 7,900
watercolour
Shanti Panchal

1118 FALLEN TREE WITH MISTLETOE £ 8,000
oil
Olwyn Bowey RA

1119 THREE DIODES £ 375
oil on board
Tom Mole

1120 LONELY HEARTS CLUB £ 2,500
watercolour
Cherryl Fountain

1121 PORTABLE CITY CONSTRUCTION £ 750
bakelite, metal and acrylic on wood
Helen Wilde

1122 VIEW OVER FLORENCE FROM VILLA £ 6,500
OMBRELLINO
oil
Christopher Johnson

1123 UNTITLED £ 1,200
oil
Julian Gordon Mitchell

1124 SPACE ANGEL, MARS AND SPIRAL GALAXY £ 1,900
acrylic and gold leaf on paper
Linda Sutton

1125 ASPARAGUS £ 10,000
egg tempera on board
David Tindle RA

1126 RUN LIKE THE WIND £ 650
oil
Tom Strupinski

1127 OPEN WIDE £ 2,000
oil
Lucy Pratt

1128	**LOVERS BY THE SEA, 2007** *oil* John Bellany RA	£ 35,000
1129	**THE LOVING KIND** *acrylic* Christopher Noulton	£ 1,200
1130	**ALDEBURGH BEACH, SOUTH** *oil on muslin board* Delia Tournay-Godfrey	£ 750
1131	**DUSK COMES** *oil on linen* June Redfern	£ 1,850
1132	**TWO BLUES, JACKET ON CHAIR** *acrylic on cotton* David Tindle RA	£ 10,000
1133	**CHINESE LANTERNS** *oil* Olwyn Bowey RA	£ 8,000
1134	**SUMMER** *mixed media* Henry Kondracki	£ 2,500
1135	**TOKYO SUBWAY** *acrylic* Carl Randall	£ 22,000
1136	**THE ESCAPEGOAT** *acrylic on board* Cyril Croucher	£ 2,900
1137	**LOST VILLAGE** *watercolour and gouache on paper* Lilo Fromm	£ 900
1138	**THE RIVER CLEDDAU MERGES LAND** AND SKY, WALES *oil on linen on board* Maurice Sheppard	£ 2,200

1139 SUMMER £ 6,000
oil
Sarah Armstrong-Jones

1140 DRAWING £ 1,500
pencil, chalk and wash
Paul Newland

1141 FISHING BEACH £ 350
acrylic on board
Paul Liddiard

1142 ROWS OF HOUSES, ITUPORANGA £ 320
oil on card
Tadeusz Deregowski

1143 UFFINGTON WHITE HORSE £ 1,400
oil
David Payne

1144 PROOF OF IDENTITY £ 180
etching and monoprint
Anthony Spencer
(edition of 30: £120 each)

1145 OBJETS PERDUS £ 500
mixed media
Stuart Wroe

1146 NIGHT BUS, BISHOPSGATE £ 525
pencil
Timothy Hyman RA

1147 THE UNLOVED £ 975
graphite
Saul Robertson

1148 COSTAS £ 1,500
charcoal
Fergus McHardy

1149 COMPLETED SHARD, LONDON BRIDGE QUARTER £ 11,500
conte crayon
Jeanette Barnes

1150 FARM CLEGYR BOIA, PEMBROKESHIRE £ 1,850
acrylic and collage
David Humphreys

1151 AFTER ATGET 3, PARC DE SAINT-CLOUD £ 280
charcoal and fixative
Carla Groppi

1152 PORTRAIT OF TRAVIS £ 2,500
graphite
Nancy Fletcher

1153 FROM NEO BANKSIDE £ 10,000
watercolour
Chris Orr RA

1154 ROCKING HORSE £ 850
oil on board
Simon Wright

1155 PIANO ÉTUDE NO. 2 £ 195
pen and ink
Jane Barton

1156 UNTITLED (FROM THE SERIES 'BLURRED TIMES') £ 1,950
photograph
Virgilio Ferreira

1157 ABOVE PIENZA £ 3,200
charcoal
Terry McAllister

1158 LUNDY £ 1,100
charcoal and graphite
Caroline McAdam Clark

1159 MAOBINO 0.1 £ 3,400
oil on paper
Issa Salliander

1160 HORIZON £ 350
pencil
Nicholas Ball

1161 WHITE SHANGHAINESE PAPER BRIDE NFS
oil
Zeng Chuanxing

1162 SAINT CLAIRE £ 1,500
charcoal
Fergus McHardy

1163 STUDY OF SHOEBILL £ 9,000
pencil, ink and gouache
Elizabeth Butterworth

1164 SIX FIGS £ 2,950
gouache and acrylic on board
Dylan Waldron

1165 CLUMSY TOURIST ROBOT AT EASTBOURNE £ 2,000
oil on board
Raymond Campbell

1166 STRANGE FLOWERS £ 550
collage with mixed media
William Pullen

1167 SLATE SKY £ 850
oil
Carol Roundhill

1168 THORN HEDGE £ 2,000
oil on board
Bridget Keen

1169 GHOSTS IN THE NURSERY £ 495
oil
Mary Barnes

1170 SOLFATARA £ 875
mixed media
Susan Gradwell

1171 CLOSING DOWN £ 950
acrylic and pen
Deborah Jane Batt

1172	**DAISY NOOK FAIR** *oil* Cliff Murphy	£ 2,400
1173	**IN BETWEEN THE TIDES** *oil* William Bowyer RA	£ 5,000
1174	**BOAT** *oil on board* Simon Wright	£ 900
1175	**EVENING SHADOWS, ST IVES** *oil* Mark McLaughlin	£ 1,250
1176	**Y LLIWEDD, SNOWDONIA** *watercolour* Roger Allen	£ 1,800
1177	**DREAM** *acrylic* Anna Maria Lovely	£ 2,100
1178	**ARCHES, ADDIS ABABA STATION I** *oil* Anthony Eyton RA	£ 19,000
1179	**THE WATER VILLAGE, CHINA, 2003** *oil* John Bellany RA	£ 25,000
1180	**CAROUSEL** *charcoal* Serena Rowe	£ 950
1181	**BLYTHBURGH CHURCH OR THE QUEEN OF THE MARSHES** *oil* William Bowyer RA	£ 8,000
1182	**PROPHET AND PROFIT** *acrylic* Roger Makk	£ 500

1183	**A CONTEMPORARY LOOK I** *oil* Sophie Levi	£ 2,500
1184	**DENNY'S, PALM CANYON DRIVE** *oil* Danny Markey	£ 12,000
1185	**THE STREETS WHERE I LIVED** *acrylic* Tony Francis	£ 850
1186	**THE POET'S FLOATING WORLD,** **HE DREAMS, HE SLEEPS** *oil on linen on board* Maurice Sheppard	£ 2,200
1187	**THE LOGGIA UDINE** *oil* Ken Howard RA	£ 7,000
1188	**FONT WALL MOJACAR** *found objects and mixed media on board* Will Maclean	£ 18,000
1189	**BEFORE THE DAY IS OVER** *gouache and tempera* Mick Rooney RA	£ 8,750
1190	**FEBRUARY SKY, CAMBER** *oil* Frederick Cuming RA	£ 4,500
1191	**THE OPEN AIR** *oil on panel* Michael de Bono	£ 6,500
1192	**LIVING UNDER BLUE SKIES, AUTUMN SUN** *oil and graphite on panel* Judith Green	£ 1,400
1193	**HEDGEROW** *oil* Jane Wormell	£ 8,000

1194 WHITE LIGHT IN MARCH, II   £ 1,600
oil on panel
Louise Balaam

1195 TWO VALLEYS   £ 950
acrylic
Tony Scrivener

1196 THE LOGGIA UDINE, REFLECTIONS   £ 38,000
oil
Ken Howard RA

1197 THE ROAD TO ITHACA   £ 12,500
oil
Philip Sutton RA

1198 THE PAINTERS' WORLD IS A PARADISE!!   £ 12,500
oil
Philip Sutton RA

1199 AFTER ATGET 2, PARC DE SAINT-CLOUD, ABRE   £ 2,700
charcoal and fixative
Carla Groppi

1200 STOREYVILLE III   £ 30,000
watercolour
David Remfry RA

1201 SANTA MARIA DEL GIUDICE   £ 15,000
egg tempera
David Tindle RA

1202 BOUNTEOUS SEA   £ 200,000
oil
John Bellany RA

1203 WHIRLING AND SWIRLING   £ 29,400
oil
Bill Jacklin RA

1204 S. MARCO QUARTET II   £ 18,000
oil on board
Ken Howard RA

1205 S. MARCO QUARTET I £ 18,000
oil on board
Ken Howard RA

1206 MADELEINE NFS
oil
Anne-Marie Butlin

1207 DAILY COMMUTE £ 995
oil on paper
Robert E. Wells

1208 TWO BOYS SUNBATHING £ 995
oil on paper
Robert E. Wells

1209 THE EVACUEES AT THE PREP. SCHOOL, 1939 NFS
monoprint with mixed media
Gillian Kogan

1210 SONNY JIMS 1942 £ 500
oil and beeswax on plywood
Rae Hope

1211 GREY WING £ 20,000
conté, pencil, ink and gouache
Elizabeth Butterworth

1212 RED SOCKS £ 2,000
oil on board
Danny Markey

1213 SEATED NUDE £ 950
pigment and watercolour
David Brayne

1214 THE RED DRESS £ 2,250
oil
Mary Carter

1215 ERIN (AN OLD ROMANIAN WOMAN) £ 450
oil
Ivanka Kutner

1216 THE COUNTRY DREAMER £ 7,400
oil on panel
Michael de Bono

1217 OPHELIA'S SPIRIT £ 350
oil
Rodney Cardiff

1218 RED GOWN £ 1,200
oil on wood
Alan Freney

1219 THE MILKMAN, PUSHKAR £ 950
oil on gold leaf
Glenny Thomas

1220 SNEAKY SLURP £ 1,200
oil
Lucy Pratt

1221 DANCE £ 2,000
oil on board
Susan Bower

1222 DEPTFORD MARKET £ 250
acrylic on wood
Terry Sole

1223 SAFE HAVEN £ 1,500
acrylic
Mick Davies

1224 MISS VAN DELFT £ 1,500
oil
Stella Parsons

1225 QUEUE £ 5,600
oil
Benjamin Sullivan

1226 PICTURA (AFTER FRANS VAN MIERIS) £ 12,450
oil on copper
Stuart Morle

1227	**COMMITTED**	£ 855
	oil on board	
	John Clark	

1228	**GHOST**	£ 1,400
	casein	
	Kate Montgomery	

1229	**SHANGHAI GIRL II**	£ 22,000
	acrylic	
	Cheung Xiangming	

1230	**SNOW 5TH AVENUE**	£ 21,000
	oil	
	Bill Jacklin RA	

1231	**CHISWICK HIGH ROAD**	£ 5,000
	oil	
	William Bowyer RA	

1232	**WATER LILY**	£ 1,850
	oil on linen	
	June Redfern	

1233	**MOMENTO**	£ 3,500
	oil on copper	
	George Melling	

1234	**GOLDFINGER SEVEN (WITH LE CORBUSIER FLAKING PAINT FROM APARTMENT STUDIO)**	£ 14,750
	oil	
	Peter Wylie	

1235	**SEEING BIG BEN THROUGH THE WHEEL**	£ 4,200
	oil on board	
	Timothy Hyman RA	

1236	**LUNCHTIME SWIM**	£ 5,000
	oil	
	William Bowyer RA	

1237	**MAIDEN CASTLE**	£ 1,400
	oil	
	David Payne	

1238 DELVES		£ 580
painted paper collage and pencil		
Paul Sutton		

1239 UNTITLED 2		£ 3,700
oil		
Jay Oliver		

1240 LET'S FACE IT		£ 7,500
oil		
George Underwood		

1241 WATERFALL ROAD		£ 500
oil on board		
Kate Wilson		

1242 BRIGHTON'S BANDSTAND ON WOOD		£ 60
photograph transferred onto wood		
Angela Newman		

1243 TOY TRUCK		£ 2,400
oil		
Comhghall Casey		

1244 THE TEMPTATION OF SAINT KEVIN OF GLENDALOUGH		£ 11,500
oil		
Thomas Ryan		

1245 FRIDAY NIGHT AT MOIRA'S		NFS
oil		
Timothy Hyman RA		

1246 TAKE AWAY		£ 9,500
acrylic		
Angela Braven		

1247 A COUNTRY WEDDING		£ 3,000
oil on hardboard with brass rods		
Anthony Green RA		

1248 NOTRE DAME FROM QUAI DU MARCHE NEUF		£ 15,000
oil on board		
Ken Howard RA		

1249	**THE RED HAT** *oil* Mary Carter	£ 1,950
1250	**CHAPEL** *oil on board* Bronwen Malcolm	£ 1,400
1251	**TREE OF WANK** *oil* Timothy Hyman RA	£ 1,155
1252	**WINDOW WITH REFLECTED SELF-PORTRAIT** *egg tempera* David Tindle RA	£ 8,500
1253	**UNSETTLED KITCHEN** *oil* Mick Rooney RA	£ 4,250
1254	**GIRL WITH A MANAGERIE** *gouache and tempera* Mick Rooney RA	£ 9,500
1255	**KENSINGTON GARDENS, 18 JANUARY** *oil on paper* Eileen Hogan	£ 22,000
1256	**KESKEYS** *acrylic on panel* Stewart Geddes	£ 1,850
1257	**FARM TREGINNIS, PEMBROKESHIRE** *acrylic and collage* David Humphreys	£ 3,500
1258	**IN THE WALLED GARDEN** *oil* David Imms	£ 5,500
1259	**TRAPEZE** *oil* Eileen Cooper RA	£ 18,000

1260	**SHE AND THE TREE** *oil* Mick Rooney RA	£ 7,500
1261	**THE SAINTLY DOG** *gouache and tempera* Mick Rooney RA	£ 3,950
1262	**AMONG THE MEMORIES** *oil* Mick Rooney RA	£ 4,250
1263	**KLORIS BY ZAHA HADID FOR ROVE GALLERY** *fibreglass with metallic finish* Dame Zaha Hadid RA (edition of 12)	£ 450,000
1264	**THE QUEEN'S JUBILEE STATUE – THE YOUNG QUEEN** *bronze* James Butler RA	£ 15,000

X

**The works in Gallery X form the series
'The Vanity of Small Differences'**

List of
Exhibitors

Abbaro, Besheer, Flat B, 4 Osborne Road, London N13 5PS,
402

ABRAHAMS, Prof. Ivor, RA, 33 Artillery Road, Ramsgate,
Kent CT11 8PT, **116, 171, 691, 697, 707, 918**

ABRAMOVIC, Marina, HON RA, Courtesy of Lisson Gallery,
52-54 Bell Street, London NW1 5BU, **934**

ACKROYD, Prof. Norman, CBE RA, 1 Morocco Street,
London SE1 3HB, **95, 222, 223, 229, 230, 231**

A'Court, Angela, 134 East 92nd Street, New York 10128,
United States of America, **649**

AL_A, 14A Brewery Road, London N7 9NH, **775**

Aldridge, Pamela, 34 Reigate Road, Brighton BN1 5AH, **325**

Alexander, Mark, c/o Wilkinson Gallery, 50-58 Vyner Street,
London E2 9DQ, **588, 939**

Alexieva, Stiliana, Flat C, 2nd Floor, 54 Lots Road, London
SW10 0QD, **153**

Allchurch, Emily, 4A Queen Mary Road, London SE19 3NW,
1027

Allen, Guy, Summer House Farm, Sharp Street, Catfield,
Norfolk NR29 5AF, **310**

Allen, Roger, Hoe Grange, Brassington, Matlock, Derbyshire
DE4 4HP, **1176**

Allen, Tim, Flat 9, Steeple Court, Coventry Road, London
E1 5QZ, **579**

Allford Hall Monaghan Morris, Morelands Ltd,
5-23 Old Street, London EC1V 9HL, **874**

ALSOP, Prof. Will, OBE RA, All Design, 42 Elcho Street,
London SW11 4AU, **882**

Altenburger, Ekkehard, APT studios, 6 Creekside, London
SE8 4SA, **439**

Amin Taha Architects, 15 Clerkenwell Close, London
EC1R 0AA, **866**

Anatsui, El, Courtesy of October Gallery, 24 Old Gloucester
Street, London WC1N 3AL, **3**

ARAD, Ron, RA, Ron Arad Associates, 62 Chalk Farm Road,
London NW1 8AN, **593, 594, 598**

Archer, Magda, c/o Polite, Canalside, Clarence Mill,
Bollington, Cheshire SK10 5JZ, **565, 640**

Arendt, Bartek, 65A Amhurst Road, London E8 1LL, **596**

B

BARLOW, Phyllida, RA, Courtesy of Hauser & Wirth,
23 Savile Row, London W1S 2ET, **706**

Barnes, Jeanette, 12 Crestbrook Place, Green Lanes, London
N13 5SB, **1149**

Barnes, Mary, 70 London Road, Stony Stratford, Milton
Keynes MK11 1JL, **1057, 1169**

Barratt, Mychael, 18 Birchwood Avenue, London N10 3BE,
250, 354

Barrett, Margaret, 71 Dornden Drive, Langton Green,
Tunbridge Wells, Kent TN3 0AG, **845**

Barron, Catherine, c/o Panter and Hall, 27 Bury Street,
London SW1Y 6AL, **968, 1095**

Bartlett, Adrian, 132 Kennington Park Road, London
SE11 4DJ, **375**

Bartlett, John, 110 Green Lanes, London N16 9EH, **470**

Barton, Jane, 23 Melrose Avenue, Wimbledon Park, London
SW19 8BU, **1155**

Batakov, Nikolai, Kolesnikova 11, Kaliningrad, 236010, Russia,
267, 268

Bates, James, 97A Bravington Road, London W9 3AA, **436**

Batoeva, Stefania, 80A Naylor Road, London SE15 1QQ, **535**

Batt, Deborah Jane, 45 The Terrace, Wokingham, Berks
RG40 1BP, **1171**

Battershell, Hannah, 46 Sybourn Street, London E17 8HA, **901**

Battye, Philippa, 6 Swan Yard, London N1 1SD, **842, 847**

Baumann, Steven, 25a Lowman Road, London N7 6DD, **802**

Baumgartner, Christiane, Courtesy of Alan Cristea Gallery,
31 & 34 Cork Street, London W1S 3NU, **429**

Baxter, Glen, c/o Flowers Gallery, 82 Kingsland Road,
London E2 8DP, **182, 651**

BEATTIE, Basil, RA, 1 Village Schoolhouse, Lower Green
West, Mitcham, Surrey CR4 3AF, **731**

Bekavac-Kononenko, Jadranka, 1 Arundel Gardens,
Winchmore Hill, London N21 3AG, **314**

BELLANY, Dr John, CBE RA, c/o Beaux Arts London,
22 Cork Street, London W1S 3NA, **1081, 1109, 1128, 1179,
1202**

Bennetts Associates Architects, 1 Rawstorne Place, London
EC1V 7NL, **877**

BENSON, Prof. Gordon, OBE RA, 40 Charlton Kings Road, London NW5 2SA, **909, 910, 911, 912, 913, 914**

Berry, June, 45 Chancery Lane, Beckenham, Kent BR3 6NR, **1089**

BEVAN, Tony, RA, c/o Ben Brown Fine Arts, 52 Brook's Mews, 1st Floor, London W1K 4EE, **88, 97, 733, 944**

Biddulph, Jacki, 51A Belsize Avenue, London NW3 4BN, **390**

Biggs, Les, Flat One, 43 Wetherby Road, Leeds LS8 2JU, **339**

Birch, Lesley, 11 Clifton Place, York, North Yorkshire YO30 6BJ, **1091**

Birds Portchmouth Russum Architects, Unit G11, Union Wharf, 23 Wenlock Road, London N1 7SB, **863**

Birnbaum, Aimee, 12 St Mark's Crescent, London NW1 7TS, **351**

BLACKADDER, Dame Elizabeth, DBE RA, c/o Royal Academy of Arts, **44, 72, 108**, c/o Glasgow Print Studio, 103 Trongate, Glasgow G1 5HD, **190, 197, 198**

BLAKE, Prof. Sir Quentin, CBE RDI HON FELLOW RA, Courtesy of Marlborough Fine Art Ltd, 6 Albemarle Street, London W1S 4BY, **178, 188, 199**

Blustin, A. J., 5 Cloughmore House, Trafalgar Street, Cambridge CB4 1ET, **464**

Bock, Elke, 23 Barrington Road, London N8 8QT, **1034**

Boele-Keimer, Vera, 48 Kingsdown Parade, Bristol BS6 5UF, **501**

Boepple, Willard, c/o Broadbent Gallery, 2nd Floor Suite, 4 Cromwell Place, London SW7 2JE, **11**

Boglietti, Giulia, Clergy House, 9 Pekin Street, London E14 6EZ, **761**

Bonomini, Paul, 4 Thornlaw Road, London SE27 0SA, **840**

Bousfield, Neil, Lokeside Cottage, Common Road, Hempstead, Norwich, Norfolk NR12 0DQ, **265, 266**

Bower, Susan, Larchfield House, Church Street, Barkston Ash, Tadcaster, North Yorkshire LS24 9PJ, **1075, 1221**

BOWEY, Olwyn, RA, c/o Royal Academy of Arts, **34, 699, 1118, 1133**

BOWLING, Frank, OBE RA, c/o Hales Gallery, Tea Building, 7 Bethnal Green Road, London E1 6LA, **47, 73, 728**

BOWYER, William, RA, 12 Cleveland Avenue, London
W4 ISN, **687, 1054, 1173, 1181, 1231, 1236**

Boyd & Evans, c/o Flowers Gallery, 82 Kingsland Road,
London E2 8DP, **978, 979**

Boyle, Lucy, 10 Roydon Close, London SW11 5BE, **645**

Braven, Angela, Harpsichord House, Cobourg Place,
Hastings, East Sussex TN34 3HY, **1246**

Brayne, David, 4 Enfield Terrace, Weymouth Road,
Evercreech, Somerset BA4 6JE, **1114, 1213**

Bremner, John, 103 Lightfoot Road, London N8 7JL, **722**

Brennan, Jessie, Flat 8, ACME Studios, 30 Gillender Street,
London E14 6RH, **64, 295**

Brett, Benjamin, The Shrubbery, Willow Lane, Norwich,
Norfolk NR2 1EU, **653**

Brewster, Claire, c/o TAG Fine Arts, Business Design Centre,
52 Upper Street, London N1 0QH, **138**

Bridgland, Sarah, Dodys Cottage, The Dale, Bonsall,
Matlock, Derbyshire DE4 2AY, **1103**

Brockbank, Sadie, 1 Mortimer Hill, Mortimer, Reading,
Berkshire RG7 3PW, **745**

Broe, Jane, 63 Woodford Crescent, Pinner, Middlesex
HA5 3UA, **563**

Brown, Don, c/o Paul Stolper Gallery, 31 Museum Street,
London WC1A 1LH, **949**

Brown, Hannah, 34 Multon House, Shore Place, London
E9 7QD, **629, 630**

Browne, Piers, Heugh, Nappa Scar, Askrigg, Leyburn, North
Yorkshire DL8 3JY, **526**

Brownlow, Marina, 992 Avenida de las Campanas, Santa Fe,
New Mexico 87507, United States of America, **469, 476**

Bryce, John, 37 Copse Avenue, Weybourne, Farnham, Surrey
GU9 9EA, **346, 410**

Buckley, Benjamin, 72 Bartholomew Road, London NW5 2AL,
493

Buckmaster-French, Hodgkyns, Brook Road, Aldham,
Essex CO6 3RW, **155**

Burder, Simon, 7 Hotham Road, London SW19 1BS, **377, 378**

Burke, Ian, 3 Gullivers, Eton College, Windsor, Berkshire
SL4 6DB, **393, 438**

Burton, Lindy, 3 Brampton Mews, Pound Lane, Marlow SL7 2SY, **660**

Burtynsky, Edward, c/o Flowers Gallery, 82 Kingsland Road, London E2 8DP, **983**

Bustin, Jane, 1 Hillside Gardens, London N6 5SU, **885**

BUTLER, James, MBE RA, Valley Farm, Radway, Warwick CV35 OUJ, **696, 925, 957, 1264**

Butlin, Anne-Marie, 12A Lightfoot Road, London N8 7JN, **1206**

Butt, Pauline, 11 Dukes Avenue, London W4 2AA, **657**

Butterworth, John, 10 Railway Avenue, Whitstable, Kent CT5 1LJ, **401**

Butterworth, Elizabeth, Lane End, Hollycross, Crazies Hill, Wargrave, Berkshire RG10 8QB, **1163, 1211**

C

Cadbury, Belinda, c/o Bartha Contemporary Ltd, 25 Margaret Street, London W1W 8RX, **583**

Calypso, Juno, 62 Malvern Road, London E8 3LJ, **969**

CAMP, Jeffery, RA, c/o Art Space Gallery, Michael Richardson Contemporary Art, 84 St Peter's Street, London N1 8JS, **65, 66, 67, 68, 69, 70**

Campbell, Gavin, 4 St Andrews Croft, Alwoodley, Leeds LS17 7TP, **453**

Campbell, Raymond, Mill House, Dad's Hill, Cross-in-Hand, Heathfield, East Sussex TN21 OSY, **1165**

Canning, Neil, c/o Advanced Graphics London, 32 Long Lane, London SE1 4AY, **513**

Cao, Henry, 30 Northern Avenue, London N9 9QJ, **746**

Cardiff, Rodney, 53 Viney's Yard, Bruton, Somerset BA10 OEU, **1217**

CARO, Sir Anthony, OM CBE RA, c/o Royal Academy of Arts, **10, 110, 125, 131**

Caro, Ben, 21 Hugo Road, London N19 5EU, **414**

Caro, Emma, 21 Hugo Road, London N19 5EU, **416**

Carpanini, David L., Fernlea, 145 Rugby Road, Milverton, Leamington Spa, Warwickshire CV32 6DJ, **1113**

Carrick, Nick, 69 Grange Road, Hove, Sussex BN3 5HW, **631**

Carter, Andrew, 44 Landells Road, London SE22 9PQ, **514**

CARTER, John, RA, Courtesy of The Redfern Gallery,
20 Cork Street, London W1S 3HL, **4, 5, 721, 768, 769**

Carter, Mary, 2 Hodges Cottages, Hemyock, Cullompton,
Devon EX15 3RW, **1214, 1249**

Carter, Tony, 2 Little Brownings, London SE23 3XJ, **878**

Casey, Comhghall, 127 Nephin Road, Cabra, Dublin 7,
Ireland, **1243**

Chambers, Derek, 8 South Entrance, Saxmundham, Suffolk
IP17 1DQ, **379, 380**

CHAMBERS, Stephen, RA, 31 Sotheby Road, London
N5 2UP, **257, 364, 365, 366, 932, 933**

Channer, Nichelle, 53 Mount Pleasant Road, London
SE13 6RD, **844**

Cheney, Barbara, 9 St Johns Road, Lower Weston, Bath,
Somerset BA1 3BN, **558**

Chesterman, Merlyn, 2 Harton Manor, The Square, Hartland,
Devon EX39 6BL, **468**

Chetwood, Laurie, 12-13 Clerkenwell Green, London
EC1R 0QJ, **816**

Cheung, Gordon, Courtesy of Alan Cristea Gallery,
31 & 34 Cork Street, London W1S 3NU, **145, 148**

CHIPPERFIELD, Prof. Sir David, CBE RA, David
Chipperfield Architects, 11 York Road, London SE1 7NX,
862, 916

Chmutin, Konstantin, c/o 13 Cotswold Road, Bristol BS3 4NX,
302

Chrisostomou, Petros, 21 Jubilee Court, Spring Lane, London
N10 3AQ, **966**

Christensen, Catalina, 6 Henley Drive, Kingston upon
Thames, Surrey KT2 7EB, **505**

Christiansen, Lesley, 3 Evelyn Mansions, Carlisle Place,
London SW1P 1NH, **415**

CHRISTOPHER, Ann, RA, c/o Royal Academy of Arts,
708, 711, 712, 736

Chuanxing, Zeng, c/o Tanya Baxter Contemporary,
436 Kings Road, London SW10 0LJ, **1161**

Churchill, Coral, 87 Lionel Road North, Brentford, Middlesex
TW8 9QZ, **599, 638**

Ciplak, Gulcehre, 24 Rodney Way, Collier Row, Romford,
Essex RM7 8PD, **580**

Clancy, Niamh, c/o 1 Morocco Street, London SE1 3HB, **421**

Clark, John, 11 Aylestone Road, Cambridge CB4 1HF, **1227**

Clark, Sara, 75 Brixton Close, Hull, Yorkshire HU8 0QL, **258, 260**

CLARKE, Carey, HON MEMBER EX OFFICIO PPRHA, 16 Joyce Avenue, Foxrock, Dublin 18, Ireland **1072**

Clarke, Jeff, 17 Newton Road, Oxford OX1 4PT, **511**

Clarke, Leigh, 48 Besford House, Pritchards Road, London E2 9BJ, **275**

Close, Chuck, c/o White Cube LLP, 48 Hoxton Square, London N1 6PB, **930**

Cloutier, Sarah, 10615 Briar Forest 801, Houston, Texas 77042, United States of America, **552**

Clutterbuck, Camilla, 3 New Cottages, Solesbridge Lane, Rickmansworth, Hertfordshire WD3 6AD, **344**

Cobb, John, 3 Hackney Terrace, Melton, Woodbridge, Suffolk IP12 1NN, **744**

COCKRILL, Prof. Maurice, RA, 78B Park Hall Road, London SE21 8BW, **71, 670, 685, 686, 689, 690**

Coldwell, Paul, 86 Oakfield Road, London N4 4LB, **509, 510**

Cole, Austin, 135 Linkfield Road, Isleworth TW7 6QW, **404, 516**

Coleman, Hen, 155 Reading Road, Henley-on-Thames, Oxfordshire RG9 1DP, **136**

Coleman, Rebecca, 11 Mayfield Road, London E17 5RH, **270, 272**

Collini, Liz, 29 Methuen Park, London N10 2JR, **308**

Connolly, Anthony, Old Bridzor, Wardour, Tisbury, Salisbury, Wiltshire SP3 6RG, **291**

COOK, Prof. Sir Peter, RA, 54 Compayne Gardens, London NW6 3RY, **835, 836, 850**

COOPER, Eileen, RA, Art First Gallery, 21 Eastcastle Street, London W1W 8DD, **121, 122, 187, 189, 196, 1259**

Cornford, Jane, Kings Head House, The Street, Hothfield, Kent TN26 1ES, **1074**

Cossey, Mary, 38 Kings Hall Road, Beckenham, Kent BR3 1LS, **185, 515**

COX, Stephen, RA, Lower House Farm, Coreley, Ludlow, Shropshire SY8 3AS, **98, 100, 101, 812, 872**

CRAIG-MARTIN, Michael, CBE RA, Courtesy of Alan
Cristea Gallery, 31 & 34 Cork Street, London W1S 3NU,
496, 497, 498, 754, Courtesy of Gagosian Gallery, London,
684, 943

Croucher, Cyril, 2 Bullock Market Terrace, Penzance,
Cornwall TR18 2PU, **1136**

CULLINAN, Edward, CBE RA, Cullinan Studio,
5 Baldwin Terrace, London N1 7RU, **829**

CUMING, Frederick, RA HON DLITT, The Gables,
Wittersham Road, Iden, Rye, East Sussex TN31 7UY,
35, 112, 1190

CUMMINS, Gus, RA, Harpsichord House, Cobourg Place,
Hastings, Sussex TN34 3HY, **117, 127, 129**

Cutler, Sally, 25A Gairloch Road, London SE5 8NG, **419**

D

Daltry, Hilary, 20 Mildmay Grove South, London N1 4RL,
525, 532

Daltry, Susan, 18 Langley Street, Langley, Norwich, Norfolk
NR14 6AD, **524**

Dalwood, Dexter, Courtesy of Alan Cristea Gallery,
31 & 34 Cork Street, London W1S 3NU, **345**

Daniell, Ian, Flat 4, 194 Peckham Rye, London SE22 9QA, **545**

DANNATT, Prof. Trevor, RA, Dannatt, Johnson Architects,
52C Borough High Street, London SE1 1XN, **813, 828**

Dant, Adam, 15 Club Row, London E2 7EY, **149, 249**

Davenport, Ian, Courtesy of Alan Cristea Gallery,
31 & 34 Cork Street, London W1S 3NU, **443**

David, Susie, Home Farm, Churchstow, Kingsbridge,
Devon TQ7 3QR, **992**

Davidson, Martin, 35 Elder Avenue, London N8 8PS, **485, 486**

DAVIE, Alan, RA, c/o Gimpel Fils, 30 Davies Street, London
W1K 4NB, **80, 81, 82, 83, 84, 89**

Davies, Mick, 171 Highbury Hill, London N5 1TB, **1223**

Davies, Richard, North Space, Salamander Court,
135 York Way, London N7 9LG, **1032, 1033**

Davis, Jon-Paul, 5 Inverhouse Gardens, Inverkip PA16 0GF,
1030

Davis, Philip, 8 Carholme Road, London SE23 2HS, **456**

Dawson, Stuart, 10 Gatehouse, Blackstone Edge Old Road, Littleborough, Lancashire OL15 0JJ, **555**

de Bono, Michael, Box 4524, 6 Slington House, Rankine Road, Basingstoke, Hampshire RG24 8PH, **1191, 1216**

DE GREY, Spencer, CBE RA, 38 Stockwell Park Crescent, London SW9 0DG, **851, 856, 876**

de Monchaux, Cathy, 1 Hoxton Street, London N1 6NL, **150**

de Monchaux, Ruth, 56 Manor Avenue, London SE4 1TE, **491**

de Sade, Dolores, 10 Manse Road, London N16 7QD, **263, 264**

Dempsey, Alan Patrick, 2A Windsor Road, Poole, Dorset BH14 8SE, **449**

Deregowski, Tadeusz, 20 Thorngrove Avenue, Aberdeen AB15 7XS, **1142**

DESMET, Anne, RA, 22 Queen Anne Road, London E9 7AH, **232, 233, 234, 238, 239, 240**

DICKSON, Dr Jennifer, RA, 20 Osborne Street, Ottawa, Ontario K1S 4Z9, Canada, **522, 523, 527, 528, 529, 530**

Dijkstra, Rineke, Courtesy of the Artist, **942**

Dillon, Michael, 11 Cloudesley Place, London N1 0JA, **834**

Dimitranova, Nelly, Top Flat, 33 Savernake Road, London NW3 2JU, **191**

Dine, Jim, Courtesy of Alan Cristea Gallery, 31 & 34 Cork Street, London W1S 3NU, **211, 212**

Dixon, Jane, 334 Crescent House, Golden Lane Estate, London EC1Y 0SN, **989, 990**

Dolan, Germaine, Flat 3, 61 Old Dover Road, Canterbury, Kent CT1 3DE, **559**

Doran, Naomi, 135 Gibson Gardens, London N16 7HH, **716**

Douglas-Morris, Freya, 14 Franconia Road, London SW4 9ND, **614**

Dow Jones Architects, 39 Calbourne Road, London SW12 8LW, **867**

Doyle, Morgan, 55 Argyll Mansions, 303-323 Kings Road, London SW3 5ER, **224, 227**

DRAPER, Kenneth, RA, Carrer Gran 55A, Es Castell, Menorca, 07720, Spain, **717, 718, 726**

Drescher, Lauren, Flat 2 Royal Victoria Patriotic Building, John Archer Way, London SW18 3SX, **147**

Dring, Mike, 2 Estria Road, Edgbaston, Birmingham
B15 2LQ, **776**

Drummond, Christopher, Flat A, 8 Nelson Road,
London N8 9RU, **798**

DSDHA, 8 Iliffe Yard, London SE17 3QA, **858**

Duffin, John, 13 Marsala Road, London SE13 7AA, **318, 427**

Duncan, Stephen, 56 Mervan Road, London SW2 1DU, **466**

Dunkley, James, Flat 162, Navarino Mansions, Dalston Lane,
London E8 1LE, **644**

DUNSTAN, Bernard, RA PPRWA, 10 High Park Road, Kew,
Richmond, Surrey TW9 4BH, **22, 23, 26, 27, 29, 30**

Durrande, Olivier, 14 Rue de la Victoire, Nantes 44300,
France, **1029**

Duttson, Robin, Flat 2, 9 Prima Road, London SW9 0NA, **475**

Dyson, Anthony, 61 Hampton Road, Teddington, Middlesex
TW11 0LA, **387**

E

Eason, Ewan David, 263 Kingsland Road, London E2 8AS,
157, 905

Easton, Bella, 40 Ruskin Walk, London SE24 9LZ, **477**

Easton, Bella & Lubomirov, Iavor, 40 Ruskin Walk, London
SE24 9LZ, **152**

Eastwood, Fiona, 7 Pitchford Street, London E15 4RZ, **602**

Eastwood, Nathan, 7 Pitchford Street, London E15 4RZ, **554**

Edmunds, Diana, 52 Park Hall Road, London SE21 8BW, **796**

Edwards, Gary, 48 Cleveland Road, Brighton, East Sussex
BN1 6FG, **903**

Ekholm, Roberto, Flat 5, 3 Princess Louise Close, London
W2 1LH, **1023**

Eldridge Smerin, 17 Calico Row, Plantation Wharf, London
SW11 3TW, **759, 926**

Ellis, Edwina, Rhyd Goch, Ystrad Meurig, Ceredigion,
SY25 6AJ, **179, 180**

Ellis-Brown, Gordon, Old Kingsworthy School, Abbots
Worthy, Winchester, Hampshire SO21 1DR, **508**

Ellwood, Derek, 2 Warren Mews, London W1T 6AL, **1067**

EMIN, Prof. Tracey, CBE RA, Tracey Emin Studio/Emin
International Ltd, Tenter Ground, London E1, **183, 184,
192, 193, 194, 919**

Emma, Signe, 9 Datchet House, Virginia Road, London E2 7ND, **997**

Ensor, Adrian, 69 Grafton Way, London WIT 6JD, **1025, 1026**

Ereira-Guyer, Theodore, Flat 8, Bryan House, Rotherhithe Street, London SE16 5HB, **336**

Escofet, Miriam, The Studio at Robin Hill, George Road, Kingston upon Thames, Surrey KT2 7NU, **1102**

Escudero, Felipe, 6 Elizabeth Mews, Kay Street, London E2 8QG, **790**

Esk, Michael, 25/6 Spottiswoode Road, Edinburgh EH9 1BJ, **1076**

Eye Try, Cumberlandstraße 14, Vienna A1140, Austria, **993**

EYTON, Anthony, RA, c/o Browse and Darby, 19 Cork Street, London WIS 3LP, **33, 40, 74, 1053, 1065, 1178**

F

Factory Architecture, 69A Mildmay Road, London N1 4PU, **875**

Faine, Brad, c/o CCA Galleries, Beech Studio, Greenhills Estate, Tilford, Surrey GU10 2DZ, **448, 500**

Farley, Lucy, 324A Portobello Road, London W10 5RU, **389, 506**

Farrer, Julia, 41 Melgund Road, London N5 1PT, **371**

FARTHING, Prof. Stephen, RA, 16 John Islip Street, London SW1P 4JU, **32, 38, 107, 173**

FEDDEN, The late Mary, OBE RA PPRWA, c/o Royal Academy of Arts, **13**, Timothy Sammons Ltd, 12 Bolton Street, London W1J 8BD, **14, 16, 17, 18**

Feilden Clegg Bradley Studios, Bath Brewery, Toll Bridge Road, Bath BA1 7DE, **861**

Ferm, Marianne, 43 Cranmer Road, London E7 0JL, **499**

Ferreira, Virgilio, Flat 4, 26 Stanford Avenue, Brighton BN1 6EA, **991, 1156**

Figueirido, Josias, C / Galindra 29B, Vigo 36213, Spain, **520**

Fisher, James, c/o Eagle Gallery, 15G Farringdon Road, London EC1R 3AL, **440**

Fitzmaurice, John, 129A Newington Green Road, London N1 4RA, **623**

Fletcher, Nancy, 60A White Hart Lane, London SW13 0PZ, **1152**

Ford, Peter, 13 Cotswold Road, Windmill Hill, Bristol
BS3 4NX, **169, 176**

Ford, Ros, 47 Hill Street, Totterdown, Bristol BS3 4TS, **245**

Foskett, Wayne, 74 St John's Park, London SE3 7JP, **1035, 1036**

FOSTER OF THAMES BANK, Lord, OM RA,
Foster + Partners, Riverside, 22 Hester Road, London
SW11 4AN, **767, 839, 841**

Fotheringham, Tom, Flat 35, Charles Rowan House,
Margery Street, London WC1X 0EH, **811**

Fountain, Cherryl, Lords Lodge, Lees Court Road,
Sheldwich Lees, Faversham, Kent ME13 0ED, **1120**

Francis, Tony, Little Stocks Cottage, Stocks Road, Aldbury,
Tring, Herts HP23 5RX, **1185**

FREETH, Peter, RA, 83 Muswell Hill Road, London
N10 3HT, **323, 324, 332, 333, 341, 350**

Freney, Alan, Coastguard Lane, Strand Road, Bray, County
Wicklow, Ireland **1218**

Frennesson, Britt, 4 Haslemere Avenue, London W13 9UJ, **672**

Fromm, Lilo, c/o Artis Gallery, 7 Wesley Square, London
W11 1TP, **1137**

Fudge, Zoë, 127 Poynton Road, London N17 9SJ, **855**

Furneaux, Paul, 36 Rodney Street (2f1), Edinburgh EH7 4DX,
720

Furniss, Darren, 6 Tumbling Close, Ossett, Yorkshire
WF5 0QX, **794, 799**

Fürstova, Mila, Flat 2, 20 Lansdown Terrace, Cheltenham,
Gloucesterhire GL50 2JP, **252**

G Gadenne, Paul, Haden House, 3A Nargate Street,
Littlebourne, Kent CT3 1UH, **1100**

Galloway, Richard, 294 Upper Street, London N1 2TU,
430, 434

Gardiner, Vanessa, Lilac Cottage, Fernhill, Charmouth,
Dorset DT6 6BX, **973, 975**

Garvey, Sarah, 204 Boundary Road, London N22 6AJ, **490**

Geddes, Stewart, 8 Downs Road, Bristol BS9 3TX, **1256**

Gentry, John David, 12 Highcliff Crescent, Rochford,
Essex SS4 3HN, **460**

George, Andrew, Noone Cottage, Springers Hill, Coleford, Radstock, Somerset BA3 5LN, **1069**

Gibbons, Peter, Coachmans, Southington, Hampshire RG25 3DA, **996**

Gibbs, Jonathan, Farmhouse, Keith Marischal, Humbie, East Lothian EH36 5PA, **280**

Giles Reid Architects, 219 Sandycombe Road, Kew, Richmond TW9 2EW, **860**

Gili, Katherine, 7 The Mall, Faversham, Kent ME13 8JL, **750**

Gillespie, Sarah, Clover Cottage, Blackawton, Totnes, Devon TQ9 7BN, **611**

Girling, Sheila, 111 Frognal, London NW3 6XR, **908, 915**

Glew, Matthew, 17 Cowslip Hill, Letchworth Garden City, Hertfordshire SG6 4HN, **655**

González-Lafita Pérez, Alicia, 92B Camden High Street, London NW1 0LT, **967**

Goodman, Ben, BV Studio, 37 Philip Street, Bedminster, Bristol BS3 4EA, **285**

Gorner, Jo, 1 Winters Cottages, Blackshaw Head, Hebden Bridge, West Yorkshire HX7 7JU, **433, 442**

Gospavic, Mina, 667B Finchley Road, London NW2 2HN, **804**

Gowdy, Carolyn, 2c Maynard Close (off Cambria Street), London SW6 2EN, **412**

Gracia, Carmen, 65 Westover Road, High Wycombe HP13 5HX, **200**

Gradwell, Susan, Southview, Moorlynch, Bridgwater, Somerset TA7 9BU, **512, 1170**

Graham, Rodney, c/o Lisson Gallery, 52-54 Bell Street, London NW1 5DA, **941**

Granville, Sarah, 139 Dalling Road, London W6 0ET, **1047**

Greaves, Terry, 88 Priory Road, London N8 7EY, **483**

GREEN, Anthony, RA, c/o Whitcombe Associates, 62 Cloncurry Street, London SW6 6DU, **1064, 1104, 1105, 1111, 1112, 1247**

Green, Judith, 'Little Rock', 30 Tregony Hill, Tregony, Truro, Cornwall TR2 5RU, **1192**

Green, Katharine, 71 Hillbrow, Letchworth, Hertfordshire SG6 3RF, **561**

Grimes, Richard, 59 Leconfield Road, London N5 2RZ, **917**

GRIMSHAW, Sir Nicholas, CBE PPRA, 57 Clerkenwell Road, London ECIM 5NG, **814, 873**

Groppi, Carla, 31A Gascony Avenue, London NW6 4NB, **1151, 1199**

Grover, Martin, Flat 2, 31 Morrish Road, London SW2 4EB, **400**

Gudynas, Peter, 89 Hazelwell Crescent, Stirchley, Birmingham B30 2QE, **981**

H

HADID, Dame Zaha, DBE RA, Zaha Hadid Architects, 10 Bowling Green Lane, London ECIR 0BQ, **1263**

Hagger, Henry, 3 Vallance Road, London N22 7UD, **299**

HALL, Nigel, RA, 11 Kensington Park Gardens, London W11 3HD, **715, 734, 735, 749**

Hall, Tim, 11 Cromwell Grove, London W6 7RQ, **987**

Halley, Gay, 55 Cameron Street, Stonehaven, Kincardineshire AB39 2HS, **902**

Hambling, Maggi, CBE, 1 Broadhinton Road, London SW4 0LU, **700**

Hamdy, Patrick, 34 Peterborough Road, London SW6 3BY, **807**

Hammick, Tom, West Beam, Henley Down, Battle, East Sussex TN33 9BN, **388**

Hampson, Mark, 16 Dickens Road, Broadstairs, Kent CT10 1DX, **327, 417**

Hanley, Hilary, 21 Woodsome Road, London NW5 1RX, **394**

Hanna, Alex, 22 Trehurst Street, London E5 0EB, **618**

Hanscomb, Brian, Tor View, Limehead, St Breward, Bodmin, Cornwall PL30 4LU, **284**

Hanselaar, Marcelle, 58 Eccleston Square, London SW1V 1PH, **457**

Harban, David, 9 Angus Close, Kenilworth, Warwickshire CV8 2XH, **225**

Harding, Mike, 2 Mill Road, Salhouse, Norwich, Norfolk NR13 6QA, **984, 985**

Hargreaves, Barton, 34 Shrewsbury Lane, Shooters Hill, London SE18 3JF, **353**

Hargreaves, Ian, 108 Beamish Road, Poole, Dorset BH17 8SJ, **1055**

Harley, Anna, West End House, The Street, Ubley,
  Bristol BS40 6PJ, **168**
Harmer, Charles, 8 Cyprus Avenue, Lytham St Annes,
  Lancashire FY8 1DY, **610**
Harnett, Marie, Courtesy of Alan Cristea Gallery,
  31 & 34 Cork Street, London W1S 3NU, **1017, 1018**
Harris, Jane, 25 Lakeside Drive, Bromley, Kent BR2 8QQ,
  261, 888
Harris, Mark Yale, c/o Artworkinternational Inc.,
  1816 San Felipe Circle, Santa Fe, CA 87505, United States
  of America, **920**
Hatjoullis, Mike, 58 Heathfield Road, Wavertree, Liverpool
  L15 9HA, **276**
Havsteen-Franklin, Eleanor, 50 Marshall Avenue, St Albans
  AL3 5HS, **172, 175**
Hawdon, Paul, 9 Worts Causeway, Cambridge CB1 8RJ, **321,
  322**
Haworth, Emma, 67 Wixs Lane, London SW4 0AH, **1101**
Haxworth, Hetty, North Lodge, Fasque, Fettercairn,
  Laurencekirk, Kincardineshire AB30 1DN, **186**
Hayeem, Norman, 127 Bennetts Castle Lane, Dagenham,
  Essex RM8 3YH, **592**
Hayes, Georgia, Diamonds, Bells Yew Green, East Sussex
  TN3 9AX, **1056**
Hayward, Louise, 284 Queen's Road, London SE14 5JN, **243**
He, Weimin, 1 Belbroughton Road, Oxford OX2 6UZ, **277**
Head, Clive, c/o Marlborough Fine Art, 6 Albemarle Street,
  London W1S 4BY, **306**
Healy, Desmond, Flat 3, 40 Eglinton Hill, London SE18 3NR,
  462
Heatherwick Studio, Willing House, 356-364 Gray's Inn
  Road, London WC1X 8BH, **857, 869**
Hedgecoe, Auberon, Braywood House, 27 St Peters Road,
  Huntingdon, Cambridgeshire PE29 7AA, **368**
Hedley, Eleanor, 14 Earlom House, Margery Street, London
  WC1X 0HX, **766, 774**
Heller, Rachel, c/o Flowers Gallery, 82 Kingsland Road,
  London E2 8DP, **564**

Hemsworth, Gerard, Blacklands, 28 Hughenden Road, Hastings TN34 3TG, **536**

Henderson, Sandie M., 158 Hesketh Lane, Tarleton, Preston PR4 6AS, **386**

Herrmann, Barbara, 23 Southwood Avenue, London N6 5SA, **465**

Hewison, Vita, 58B Linden Grove, London SE15 3LF, **1028**

Hicklin, Jason, c/o Beardsmore Gallery, 22-24 Prince of Wales Road, London NW5 3LG, **356, 474**

Hicks, Rae, 8 St Olaves Gardens, London SE11 6DR, **576**

Hickson, Joan, Garden Flat, 7 Crescent Road, Kingston upon Thames KT2 7RD, **1110**

Hiles, Adam, 13 Oakley Close, Addlestone, Surrey KT15 2LT, **809, 819**

Hill, Harry, c/o Independent Talent Group, 76 Oxford Street, London W1D 1BS, **590, 591**

Hillier, Joseph, Collingdon House, 68 Collingdon Road, High Spen, Rowlands Gill, Co. Durham NE39 2EF, **533**

Hinchliffe, Peter, 66A Harrow Halls of Residence, University of Westminster, Northwick Park HA1 3TP, **825**

Hipkiss, Paul, 37 The Crescent, Cradley Heath, West Midlands B64 7JS, **362**

Ho, Wuon-Gean, Flat 2, 211A Whitechapel Road, London E1 1DE, **226**

Hobdell, Roger, 4 Woodchurch Road, London NW6 3PN, **383**

Hodes, Charlotte, 86 Oakfield Road, London N4 4LB, **478, 484**

Hogan, Eileen, 13 Wythburn Place, London W1H 7BU, **1255**

Holecz, Louisa, Calle Encinacorba no 2, Zaragoza 50012, Spain, **1013, 1014**

Holmes, David Cecil, 5 Calvert Street, London NW1 8NE, **560**

Homma, Kaori, 83 Brookbank Road, London SE13 7BZ, **135**

Honnor, Michael, 26 Church Street, South Brent, Devon TQ10 9AB, **244**

Hope, Benjamin, 157 Langton Way, London SE3 7JS, **1092**

Hope, Rae, 140 New Ridley Road, Stocksfield, Northumberland NE43 7EQ, **1210**

Hopkins, Prof. Clyde, c/o Advanced Graphics London, 32 Long Lane, London SE1 4AY, **445, 539**

HOPKINS, Sir Michael, CBE RA, Hopkins Architects,
27 Broadley Terrace, London NW1 6LG, **792**

Horner, Marguerite, 65 Rusthall Avenue, London W4 1BN,
679, 681

Horovitz, Michael, OBE, c/o New Departures / Poetry
Olympics, 29C Colville Terrace, London W11 2BU, **601**

Houser, Jonathan, Falstersvej 12, 3 Tv, Frederiksberg 2000,
Denmark, **928**

HOWARD, Ken, OBE RA, c/o Richard Green Gallery,
147 New Bond Street, London W1S 2TS, **39, 1187, 1196,
1204, 1205, 1248**

Hubbard, Steven, 1 Berkeley Villas, Lower Street, Stroud,
Gloucestershire GL5 2HU, **133, 134**

Hughes, Chris Shaw, 41 Lancing Park, Lancing, West Sussex
BN15 8RF, **806, 808**

Hughes, Tom, Hall Floor Flat, 63 Redland Road, Bristol
BS6 6AQ, **1097**

HUME, Gary, RA, c/o Royal Academy of Arts, **935**

Humphreys, David, Maudlin Hill House, Sopers Lane,
Steyning, West Sussex BN44 3PU, **1150, 1257**

Humphreys, John, Beachcrest, Normans Bay, Pevensey,
East Sussex BN24 6PS, **597**

Hunt, Helen, Mercatoria Cottage, 12A Mercatoria,
St Leonards-on-Sea, East Sussex TN38 0EB, **1106**

Hunt, Susie, Mill Farm, Kemnay, Inverurie, Aberdeenshire
AB51 5NY, **1078**

Hutton, Julia, The Front Room Studio, 110 South Street,
Bridport, Dorset DT6 3NW, **518**

HUXLEY, Prof. Paul, RA, 2 Dalling Road, London W6 0JB,
91, 92, 93, 94, 678, 682

HYMAN, Timothy, RA, 62 Myddelton Square, London
EC1R 1XX, **45, 62, 1146, 1235, 1245, 1251**

I

Imms, David, 6 Church Street, Finedon, Northamptonshire
NN9 5NA, **1258**

IRVIN, Albert, RA, c/o Advanced Graphics London,
32 Long Lane, London SE1 4AY, **213, 214**, c/o Gimpel Fils,
30 Davies Street, London W1K 4NB, **664, 675, 701**

Iwamoto, Ikuko, Unit 51 Craft Central, 33-35 St John's Square, London ECIM 4DS, **751, 752**

J

JACKLIN, Bill, RA, c/o Marlborough Fine Art Ltd, 6 Albemarle Street, London WIS 4BY, **59, 472, 473, 479, 1203, 1230**

Jackson, Davina, 7 Hillcrest Gardens, London N3 3EY, **502**

Jackson, Vanessa, 169 Bermondsey Street, London SEI 3UW, **202, 203**

Jacob, Wendy, 8 Ripplevale Grove, London NI IHU, **228, 235**

Jampel, Aileen, 19 Edmunds Walk, London N2 OHU, **450**

Jaques, Stephen, Flat 2, 34 Belvedere Road, London SEI9 2HW, **567, 646**

JARAY, Tess, RA, Lion East Apartment, 24 North Road, London N7 9EA, **48**

Jarvis, Maureena, 20 Magdalen Road, St Leonards-on-Sea, East Sussex TN37 6EP, **622**

Jarvis, Roland, Tackleway Hall, Hastings, East Sussex TN34 3BU, **994**

Jenkins, Lawrence, Fifield, 73A Dynes Road, Kemsing, Kent TNI5 6RD, **396**

Jenner, Benjamin, 16 Weston House, King Edward's Road, London E9 7SD, **665, 669**

Jerry Tate Architects, c/o Hothouse, 274 Richmond Road, London E8 3QW, **738**

Jewell, Rebecca, 21 Pages Lane, London NIO IPU, **154**

JIRICNA, Eva, CBE RA, Eva Jiricna Architects Ltd, Third Floor, 38 Warren Street, London WIT 6AE, **795, 797, 800, 865, 868**

Johnson, Christopher, I The Old Cattle Yard, Trull Farm Buildings, Tetbury, Gloucestershire GL8 8SQ, **1122**

Jokhoo, Jennifer, Flat B, 67 East Dulwich Grove, London SE22 8PR, **273**

Jonas, Christopher, 25 Victoria Square, London SWIW ORB, **1004**

JONES, Allen, RA, 41 Charterhouse Square, London ECIM 6EA, **96, 595, 946**, Courtesy of Alan Cristea Gallery, 31 & 34 Cork Street, London WIX 2NU, **215, 216, 217**

Jones, Bobbie, 2 St Anthony, Yarpole, Leominster, Herefordshire HR6 0EQ, **143**

Jones, Frederick, 28 Princes Park Mansions, Liverpool L8 3SA, **467**

Jones, Katherine, 5 Greenleaf Close, London SW2 2HB, **289, 886**

Jones, Lucy, c/o Flowers Gallery, 82 Kingsland Road, London E2 8DP, **573**

Jones, Mark, Unit 9 Block A, Fawe Street, London E14 6PD, **413, 422**

Jones, Mulberry, 22 Queen Anne's Place, Bush Hill Park, Enfield EN1 2PT, **609**

Jones, Peter, 2A Riversdale Road, London N5 2JP, **550**

Junghanns, Christian, Mars Strasse 13, Munich D-80335, Germany, **540**

K

Katz, Alex, Courtesy of the Artist and Timothy Taylor Gallery, 15 Carlos Place, London W1K 2EX **931**

Keen, Bridget, 3 Kitts Court, Chapel Street, Penzance, Cornwall TR18 4AG, **1168**

Keith Williams Architects, 17-21 Emerald Street, London WC1N 3QN, **755, 756**

Kelly, Laura, 2 Clover Hill, Herbert Road, Bray, Co. Wicklow, Ireland, **1041**

Kennedy, Michael, 107 Knights Croft, New Ash Green, Longfield, Kent DA3 8HY, **628**

Kenny, Chris, c/o England & Co, 90-92 Great Portland Street, London W1W 7NT, **141**

KERR, Dr Janette, HON MEMBER EX OFFICIO PRWA, Hill House, Church Street, Lower Coleford, Nr Radstock, Somerset BA3 5NA, **683**

Kevans, Annie, Flat 28, Heron Court, 14 Big Hill, London E5 9HH, **621**

Kha, Caroline, 29C Islip Street, London NW5 2DJ, **971**

Khan, Mohammed Abdullah Ariba, Flat 1, 75 Abbey Road, London NW8 0AE, **541**

Kidwell, Adrian, 21 Oakhill Road, Ashtead, Surrey KT21 2JG, **666, 668**

KIEFER, Anselm, HON RA, Courtesy of the Artist and White Cube, London, **667**

Kihara, Yoshimi, 18 Woodriffe Road, London E11 1AH, **1052**

Kilgour, Simon W. L., Stoke House, 22 Amersham Road, Chesham Bois, Amersham, Buckinghamshire HP6 5PE, **619**

Kilroe, Janine, 1 Benson Close, Bicester, Oxfordshire OX26 4FQ, **1003**

Kim, Shinwook, 14 Chargrove Close, London SE16 6AP, **1049**

King, Leonie, Oranmore Castle, Oranmore, Galway, Ireland, **677**

KING, Prof. Phillip, CBE PPRA, 26 Savernake Road, London NW3 2JP, **709, 710, 849**

King, Terry, 12 Napoleon Road, Twickenham TW1 3EP, **1046**

Kirk, Simon, 19 Danescroft Drive, Leigh-on-Sea, Essex SS9 4NR, **1094**

Kirkbride, Michael, 62 Hatley Close, London N11 3LN, **1108**

KIRKEBY, Per, HON RA, Courtesy of Galerie Michael Werner, Märkisch Wilmersdorf, Alte Parkstraße 3B, Trebbin 14959, Germany, **102**

Kirwan, Richard, 72 Sandmere Road, London SW4 7QH, **359**

Klein, Anita, 3 Vesta Court, City Walk, London SE1 3BP, **392**

KNEALE, Prof. Bryan, RA, 10A Muswell Road, London N10 2BG, **739, 740, 747, 778, 782, 784**

Knox, Christopher, 11 Fisher Street, Lewes, East Sussex BN7 2DG, **298**

Kogan, Gillian, 2 St Thomas's Gardens, London NW5 4EX, **1209**

Kondracki, Henry, 20 Marchmont Crescent, Edinburgh EH9 1HL, **1093, 1134**

KORALEK, Paul, CBE RA, 3 Rochester Road, London NW1 9JH, **780, 781, 785, 786, 787, 788**

Korzer-Robinson, Alexander, 102 Beaufort Road, Bristol BS5 8EG, **159, 160**

Kotecha, Nimisha, 6 Hazelbank, Croxley Green, Rickmansworth, Hertfordshire WD3 3EW, **604**

Kravitz, Roberta, 18A Belsize Grove, London NW3 4UN, **625**

Krimpas, Olivia, Upper Masionette, 23 Lambolle Road, London NW3 4HS, **204**

Kubecki, Terry, 66 Barrett Road, London E17 9ET, **531**

Kuhfeld, Cathryn, The Corner House, Upper Bridge Street, Wye, Ashford, Kent TN25 5AW, **492**

Kutner, Ivanka, 35 Brewers Buildings, Rawstorne Street, London EC1V 7NB, **1215**

Kwon, Dae Hun, 25 Dalston Lane, London E8 3DF, **741**

L

Lacy Hodge, Jane, Barefoots Farm, Hawkley, Hampshire GU33 6JR, **487**

Lamb, Matthew, Flat 3, Bosworth Court, Bath Road, Slough, Berkshire SL1 6DA, **642**

Lancaster, Mo, Rose Cottage, Taunton Road, Bishops Lydeard, Taunton, Somerset TA4 3LR, **195**

Lang, Liane, 15 Cornwall Crescent, London W11 1PH, **962, 964**

Langford, Martin, 59 Crest Gardens, Ruislip, Middlesex HA4 9HB, **340, 360**

Lanski, Martina, 8 Boleyn Way, Barnet EN5 5JS, **647**

Lawler, Teresa, 28 Woodmancourt, Godalming, Surrey GU7 2BT, **1079**

Lawrence, Peter, 48 Lonsdale Road, Oxford OX2 7EP, **164, 278**

Lawrenson, Emma, Ivy Bank Farmhouse, Sheffield Road, Jackson Bridge, Holmfirth, West Yorkshire HD9 7HB, **372**

Lawson, Simon, Flat 1, 20 Allfarthing Lane, London SW18 2PQ, **328, 455**

LE BRUN, Christopher, PRA, c/o Royal Academy of Arts, **729**

Leahy-Clark, Sharon, 187 Wellington Buildings, Ebury Bridge Road, London SW1W 8RX, **641**

Leale, Mike, 10 Mount Pleasant Crescent, Hastings, East Sussex TN34 3SG, **1001**

Lee, Chang-Yeoh, 40 Cornelia Street, London N7 8BA, **852**

Lee, Sara, 6 Westcombe Park Road, London SE3 7RB, **307, 309**

Lee, Sharon, 72 Grosvenor Terrace, London SE5 0NW, **482**

Leman, Martin, 1 Malvern Terrace, London N1 1HR, **1062**

Lennox, Garey, 24 Grenville Road, Croydon CR0 0NY, **1000**

Lerooij, Pieter, Boezingestraat 89, Elverdinge 8906, Belgium, **292**

Levi, Sophie, 17A Princess Road, London NW1 8JR, **589, 1183**

Levitas, Rachel, 261 Leahurst Road, London SE13 5LS, **521**

Levy, Valeria, 12 Elsworthy Road, London NW3 3DJ, **547**

Lewis, Stephen, 6 Creekside, London SE8 4SA, **605**

Lewis, Tim, c/o Flowers Gallery, 82 Kingsland Road,
    London E2 8DP, **315**

Li, WeiTao, Flat 3, 24 Marshalsea Road, London SE1 1HF, **820**

LIBESKIND, Daniel, HON RA, c/o Royal Academy of Arts,
    783

Liddiard, Paul, 20 Letheren Place, Old Town, Eastbourne,
    East Sussex BN21 1HL, **1141**

Lintine, David, 79A Leigham Court Drive, Leigh-on-Sea,
    Essex SS9 1PT, **363**

Litherland, Geoff Diego, 6 Mansfield Court, Mansfield Road,
    Nottingham NG5 2BW, **585**

Liu, Xiaocen, 15 The Courtyard, 1 Alt Grove, London
    SW19 4DY, **1088**

Llewellyn, Alice, 5 Allen Road, London N16 8SB, **409**

Lloyd, Jonathan, 18 Ramsey's Lane, Wooler, Northumberland
    NE71 6NR, **489**

Lodge, Jean, 52 Granville Court, Cheney Lane, Headington,
    Oxford OX3 0HS, **177**

LONG, Richard, CBE RA, Courtesy of Lisson Gallery,
    52-54 Bell Street, London NW1 5BU, **639**

Loughridge, Sally, 32 Tregarvon Road, London SW11 5QE, **181**

Lovely, Anna Maria, The Lovely Gallery, 140 Sydenham
    Road, London SE26 5JZ, **1177**

Low, Sharon, 39 St Clairs Road, Croydon, Surrey CR0 5NE,
    458, 459

Lowe, Jeff, 6A Havelock Walk, London SE23 3HG, **730, 743**

Luce, 152 Church Road, London SE19 2NT, **205**

Ludwig, Katherine Dolgy, PO Box 110480, Brooklyn,
    New York 11211, United States of America, **408**

Lydbury, Jane, 101 Humber Road, London SE3 7LW, **269**

M   Macalpine, Jean, Carrer Gran 55A, Es Castell, Menorca 07720,
            Spain, **980**

MACCORMAC, Sir Richard, CBE PPRIBA RA,
    c/o MJP Architects, 9 Heneage Street, London E1 5LJ, **803**

Macfarlane, Barbara, c/o Rebecca Hossack Gallery,
    2A Conway Street, London W1T 6BA, **889**

MACH, Prof. David, RA, 8 Havelock Walk, London
SE23 3HG, **727, 921, 922, 923**

Mackay, Tammy, 187 Lower Richmond Road, London
SW15 1HH, **382**

Mackechnie, John, 6 Holyrood Crescent, Glasgow G20 6HJ,
972, 974

Maclean, Will, 18 Dougall Street, Tayport, Fife DD6 9JD, **1188**

MacMurray, Susie, 11 Summerfield Place, Wilmslow,
Cheshire SK9 1NE, **748, 853**

Macrae, Jacqueline, 38 Overmead Drive, South Woodham
Ferrers, Chelmsford, Essex CM3 5SW, **1010**

Madeiros, Daniel, 222 Broomwood Road, London SW11 6JY,
848

Mager, Val, 17 Park Avenue, Beverley, East Yorkshire
HU17 7AT, **481**

Mahoney, Nadine, 15 Hewlett Road, London E3 5NA, **627**

Mahood, Kenneth, 79 River Court, Upper Ground,
London SE1 9PB, **144, 156**

MAINE, John, RA, Old School, Church Road, East Knoyle,
Salisbury, Wiltshire SP3 6AE, **1, 2, 6, 8, 12**

Maj Plemenitas – Linkscale, 273B Willesden Lane,
London NW2 5JG, **854**

Makk, Roger, Dolphin Cottage, Yarlington, Wincanton,
Somerset BA9 8DJ, **1182**

Malcolm, Bronwen, 108 Kennington Road, London SE11 6RE,
1250

MANASSEH, Leonard, OBE RA PPRWA, 6 Bacon's Lane,
London N6 6BL, **120, 692, 693, 694, 695, 698**

Manie, Ann, 25 Surrey Lane, London SW11 3PA, **283, 305**

Mannocci, Lino, 119 Elgin Avenue, London W9 2NR, **330, 331**

MANSER, Michael, CBE RA PPRIBA HONRAIC, The Manser
Practice, Bridge Studios, Hammersmith Bridge Road,
London W6 9DA, **822**

Mara, Alice, 6 Market Street, Lewes, East Sussex BN7 2NB,
316, 317

Marinkov, Sasa, Woodcut, Riverside, Twickenham,
Middlesex TW1 3DJ, **488**

Markey, Danny, Courtesy of The Redfern Gallery,
20 Cork Street, London W1S 3HL, **1184, 1212**

Martin, Sonia, 63B Kennington Park Road, London SE11 4JQ, **373**

Martin Williams/Hampson Williams, Unit 5, 151-153 Bermondsey Street, London SE1 3HA, **771**

Martina, Toni, 85 Harold Road, Hastings, East Sussex TN35 5NJ, **431, 432**

Massey, Nigel, Flat 6, 158 Church Road, London SE19 2NT, **504**

Maw, Alex, 43 Duke Street, Cheltenham, Gloucestershire GL52 6BS, **1096**

McAdam Clark, Caroline, 49 Larkhall Rise, London SW4 6HT, **1158**

McAllister, Terry, 3 Orpen Avenue, Belfast, County Antrim BT10 0BS, **1157**

McBeath, Norman, 4 Learmonth Gardens Mews, Edinburgh EH4 1EX, **1007, 1040**

MCCOMB, Dr Leonard, RA, Studio 4, 3 Stewart's Place, Blenheim Gardens, London SW2 5AZ, **43, 115, 118, 898, 899**

McConnell, Richard, 13 Dagmar Road, London N22 7RT, **635**

McConnie, Oliver, 72 Burton Road, London SW9 6TQ, **348**

MCFADYEN, Jock, RA, Unit 4 Helmsley Place, London E8 3SB, **46, 76, 103, 104, 105, 719**

McGuire, Emma, 20 Cavendish Mansions, Clapton Square, London E5 8HR, **1073**

McHardy, Fergus, 15 Tristan Square, London SE3 9UB, **1148, 1162**

McKay, Sally, 89 Vanbrugh Hill, London SE10 9HB, **347**

MCKEEVER, Prof. Ian, RA, c/o Royal Academy of Arts, **77, 78, 79**

MCKENZIE SMITH, Ian, CBE HON MEMBER EX OFFICIO PPRSA, Heron House, Montrose, Angus DD10 9TJ, **676**

McLaughlin, Ben, 10 Cranbourne Court, 113-115 Albert Bridge Road, London SW11 4PE, **1050**

McLaughlin, Mark, Clockwork Studios, 38A Southwell Road, London SE5 9PG, **1175**

Mead, Scott, 7 Lansdowne Crescent, London W11 2NH, **1011**

Meanley, Rebecca, 71B Graham Road, London E8 1PB, **654**

Meazza, Luciana, 68 Tredegar Road, London E3 2EP, **569**

Mehta, Sharda, 4 Fitzroy Close, London N6 6JT, **398**

Melling, George, 20 Kings Drive, Fulwood, Preston,
Lancashire PR2 3HN, **1233**

Melvin, Johanna, 20 St Barnabas Road, London E17 8JY, **562**

Merchant, Chitra, 28 Laurel Street, Kingswood, Bristol
BS15 8NB, **311, 312**

Midgley, Julia, The Hollies, 79 School Lane, Hartford,
Cheshire CW8 1PG, **329**

Miller, Heather, 141 Grove Green Road, London E11 4ED,
1008

Milner, Judy, 47 Ivanhoe Road, London SE5 8DH, **742**

MILROY, Lisa, RA, c/o Royal Academy of Arts, **87, 673, 674**

MISTRY, Prof. Dhruva, CBE RA, Grosvenor Gallery,
21 Ryder Street, London SW1Y 6PX, **737, 929**

Mistry, Navnit, 40A Somerset Road, Harrow, Middlesex
HA1 4NG, **582**

Mitchell, Julian Gordon, 57 Knox Green, Binfield RG42 4NZ,
1090, 1123

MJP Architects, 9 Heneage Street, London E1 5LJ, **864**

Mole, Tom, 84 Albert Road, London N22 7AH, **1119**

Molony, Emma, **542**

Momtahan, Antoinette, 46 Pentney Road, London SW12 0NX,
758, 762

Montgomery, Kate, 18 Farm Road, Hove, East Sussex
BN3 1FB, **1228**

Moon, Jacqueline, 21A King's Road, Twickenham TW1 2QS,
367

MOON, Mick, RA, Courtesy of Alan Cristea Gallery,
31 & 34 Cork Street, London W1S 3NU, **85**

Moon, Richard, 117C Parnell Road, London E3 2RT, **361**

Moore, Bridget, 18 Cotmandene, Dorking, Surrey RH4 2BT,
1068

Moore, Rob, 346 Park Road, Cowes, Isle of Wight PO31 7NN,
652

Morey de Morand, C., 61D Oxford Gardens, London W10 5UJ,
636

Morle, Stuart, 72 James Walk, Rialto, Dublin 8, Ireland, **1226**

Morley, Andrea, 17 Saint Michaels Crescent, Pinner HA5 5LE,
1048

Morris, David, 13 Lascelles Road, Harrogate, Yorkshire
   HG2 0LA, **454**
MORRIS, Mali, RA, APT Studios, Harold Wharf,
   6 Creekside, London SE8 4SA, **36, 61, 63, 90, 688, 702**
Moxhay, Suzanne, Flat 2, Edgehill Lodge, 153 Turnham Road,
   London SE4 2LY, **1044, 1045**
Mundy, Penny, 2 Yewtree Cottages, Jubilee Road, Chelsfield,
   Orpington, Kent BR6 7QX, **451**
Murphy, Cliff, 33 Harper Street, Oldham OL8 1BB, **1172**
Murray, Karin, 32 Somerfield Road, London N4 2JJ, **343**

N

Nadal, Judy, 74 Forest Drive West, London E11 1LA, **303**
Narita, Miyako, 18B Ashby Street, London EC1V 0ED, **976,
   1020**
NASH, David, OBE RA, Capel Rhiw, Glanypwll, Blaenau
   Ffestiniog, Gwynedd LL41 3NT, **7**
Nathan, Korin, 106 Wimbledon Park Road, London
   SW18 5UA, **620**
Neal, Arthur, 32 Duke Street, Deal, Kent CT14 6DT, **616, 633**
Newell, Jacqueline, 44 Hilltop Walk, Woldingham, Surrey
   CR3 7LG, **293, 294**
Newland, Paul, 14 Garden Street, Lewes, East Sussex BN7 1TJ,
   1140
Newman, Angela, 43 Sillwood Road, Brighton, East Sussex
   BN1 2LE, **1242**
Nisbett, Darren, 43 Pewsey Vale, Bracknell, Berkshire
   RG12 9YA, **1038, 1039**
Nix, Marianne, 9 Heath Villas, Vale of Health, London
   NW3 1AW, **441**
Norton, Lindy, 153 Park Avenue, Hull, East Yorkshire
   HU5 3EX, **418**
Noulton, Christopher, 4 Whittell Gardens, London
   SE26 4LN, **1129**
Nowak, Jan, ul. Scigaly 6/6, Katowice 40-208, Poland, **163**

O

OCEAN, Prof. Humphrey, RA, 22 Marmora Road, London
   SE22 0RX, **106, 586, 587, 937, 938**
O'DONOGHUE, Hughie, RA, c/o Marlborough Fine Art,
   6 Albemarle Street, London W1S 4BY, **128, 161, 174, 663**

O'Donovan, Nuala, 'Carrigdhoun', 5 The Grove, Shanakiel, Cork, Ireland, **313**

Oliver, Jay, 19 Stenigot Road, Lincoln, Lincolnshire, LN6 3PD, **1239**

Oliver, Marilène, c/o Beaux Arts Gallery, 22 Cork Street, London WIS 3NA, **471, 534**

Olsan, David, 35C Mornington Crescent, London NWI 7RE, **960**

O'Meara, Mary Teresa, St Johns Cottage, 1 Garden Court, Canal Street, Chester, Cheshire CHI 4HA, **549**

O'Neill, Nigel, 20 Chancery House, Lowood Street, London EI OBU, **570, 572**

Opie, Julian, Courtesy of Lisson Gallery, 52-54 Bell Street, London NWI 5DA, **936**, Courtesy of Alan Cristea Gallery, 31 & 34 Cork Street, London WIS 3NU, **986**

ORR, Prof. Chris, MBE RA, 5 Anhalt Road, London SWII 4NZ, **246, 247, 248, 253, 256, 1153**

Oshelda, Anne-Marie, The Nook, Babbs Green, Wareside, Ware, Hertfordshire SGI2 7RX, **1059**

Otto, Marshfield Screen Print, Martor Industrial Estate, Tormarton Road, Marshfield, Wiltshire SNI4 8LJ, **132**

Overill, Ralph, 10 Foxleigh, Billericay, Essex CMI2 9NS, **406, 407**

P   PALADINO, Mimmo, HON RA, c/o Royal Academy of Arts, **51**

Panchal, Shanti, IIA Graham Road, Harrow, Middlesex HA3 5RP, **1117**

Park, Heechan, Flat 47, Kings College Court, 55 Primrose Hill Road, London NW3 3EA, **777, 779**

Park, Stephen, c/o The Print Studio, Building 10, Homerton Business Centre, Purbeck Road, Cambridge CB2 8HN, **428**

PARKER, Cornelia, OBE RA, Courtesy of Frith Street Gallery, 17-18 Golden Square, London WIF 9JJ, **9, 167, 713, 714**

Parkin, Oliver, 38B Dunsmure Road, London NI6 5PW, **995**

PARRY, Eric, RA, Eric Parry Architects, 28-42 Banner Street, London ECIY 8QE, **757, 827, 832**

Parsons, Stella, 28 West End Lane, London NW6 4PA, **1224**

Parth, Irmgard, Flat 3, 55 Crewdson Road, London SW9 0LH, **170, 236**

Paul, Celia, c/o Marlborough Fine Art, 6 Albemarle Street, London WIS 4BY, **948**

Pavitt, Andrew, Flat 16 Pilgrims Cloisters, 116 Sedgmoor Place, London SE5 7RQ, **461**

Payne, David, 25 Willmers Close, Bedford MK41 8DX, **1143, 1237**

Payne, Freya, c/o Flowers Gallery, 82 Kingsland Road, London E2 8DP, **286, 290**

Paynter, Hilary, Brunswick House, Torridge Hill, Bideford, Devon EX39 2BB, **399**

Peacock, Elva, 27 The Cedars, Fleet, Hampshire GU51 3YL, **600**

Pembridge, Susan, 50 Clementina Road, London E10 7LS, **543**

Perera, Sumi, High View, 22A Fenton Road, Redhill, Surrey RH1 4BN, **271**

Perring, Susie, Halfmoon Studio, Unit B23 Parkhall Industrial Estate, 40 Martell Road, London SE21 8EN, **519**

PERRY, Grayson, RA, Courtesy of the Artist and Victoria Miro, London, Victoria Miro Gallery, 16 Wharf Road, London N1 7RW, **1265, 1266, 1267, 1268, 1269, 1270**

Petterson, Melvyn, City of London Almshouses, Flat 3, Ferndale Road, London SW98AN, **349, 480**

Peyton, Elizabeth, c/o Sadie Coles HQ, 69 South Street, London W1K 2QZ, **950, 952**

PHILLIPS, Tom, CBE RA, 57 Talfourd Road, London SE15 5NN, **111, 139, 140, 142, 953**

Pilgrem, Rennie, 3 Ashchurch Park Villas, London W12 9SP, **385**

Pincis, Kasper, Flat 2, 80 Deptford High Street, London SE8 4RT, **320**

Pittaway, Neil, 1 Glenfields, Netherton, Wakefield, West Yorkshire WF4 4SH, **463**

Poliak, Diana, The Riding Light, Gravesend Road, Sevenoaks, Kent TN15 7JJ, **411**

Poots, Sarah, 13 Beavis House, Defoe Road, London N16 0ER, **658**

Pratt, Lucy, The Cottage, 14 Church Street, Chipping Norton, Oxfordshire OX7 5NT, **1127, 1220**

Price, Felix, 8A Lancaster Avenue, London SE27 9DZ, **603**
Price & Myers, 30 Newman Street, London W1T 1LT, **791**
Prieto, Francisca, Studio E12 - Cockpit Arts, Cockpit Yard,
  Northington Street, London WCIN 2NP, **137, 158**
Prince, Rosey, 239 Malpas Road, London SE4 1BH, **296**
Pullen, William, c/o Gallery Muse, 16 Chapel Street,
  Petersfield, Hampshire GU32 3DS, **1166**

Q   Quadrat, Simon, 14 The Green, Aldbourne, Marlborough,
  Wiltshire SN8 2BW, **1082**

R   RAE, Dr Barbara, CBE RA, Adam Gallery, 24 Cork Street,
  London W1S 3NJ, **58**, CCA Galleries Ltd, The Studio,
  Greenhills Estate, Tilford Road, Tilford, Farnham,
  Surrey GU10 2DZ, **218, 219, 220, 221**
Randall, Carl, 8 Freeman Road, High Heaton, Newcastle
  upon Tyne NE7 7AH, **1135**
Ravenscroft, Ben, 101 Manwood Road, London SE4 1SA, **571,
  578**
Recordon, Nick, 63 De La Warr Road, East Grinstead
  RH19 3BS, **546, 557**
Redfern, June, 12 Lawley Street, London E5 0RJ, **1131, 1232**
Redington, Simon, 10 Maunsel Street, London SW1P 2QL, **424**
Redman, Joel, 31 Albert Park Place, Montpelier, Bristol
  BS6 5ND, **977, 982**
Reisner, Yael, Flat 1, 54 Compayne Gardens, London
  NW6 3RY, **760**
Rejs, Jolanta, 8 Sheridan Court, Sheridan Road, Frimley,
  Surrey GU16 7DX, **425, 426**
Relly, Tamsin, Flat 4, Stambourne House, Lansdowne Way,
  London SW8 2DH, **297, 342**
REMFRY, David, MBE RA, c/o Royal Academy of Arts, **895,
  896, 897, 900, 1084, 1200**
Renshaw, John, The Old School House, High Street, Malpas,
  Cheshire SY14 8PR, **544**
Richards, Nicholas, 6 Bradgate Road, London SE6 4TS,
  237, 423
Rigden, Geoffrey, 57 Reardon Street, London E1W 2QJ, **584**

RITCHIE, Prof. Ian, CBE RA, c/o Ian Ritchie Architects, 110 Three Colt Street, London E14 8AZ, **772, 773, 824, 826, 833, 870**

Rizzo, Daniela, 60B Marmion Road, London SW11 5PA, **1006**

Roberts, John, 26 Acton Road, Whitstable, Kent CT5 1JJ, **517**

Robertson, Saul, 180 Churchill Drive, Broomhill, Glasgow G11 7HA, **1080, 1147**

Robinson, Claire, 32 Aslett Street, London SW18 2BN, **1022**

Rogers, Sarah, Knockarigg Cottage, Knockarigg, Grangecon, County Wicklow, Ireland, **395**

ROGERS OF RIVERSIDE, Lord, CH RA, Rogers Stirk Harbour + Partners, Thames Wharf Studios, Rainville Road, London W6 9HA, **753, 830, 831, 837, 838, 843**

ROONEY, Mick, RA, Courtesy of The Fosse Gallery, Manor House, The Square, Stow-on-the-Wold, Cheltenham, Gloucestershire GL54 1AF, **1189, 1253, 1254, 1260, 1261, 1262**

Rose, Angela, Flat 14 Everett Court, Watling Street, Radlett, Hertfordshire WD7 7NG, **607**

Roundhill, Carol, 238 Trinity Road, London SW18 3RQ, **1167**

Rowe, Serena, 1 Shaftesbury Mews, London SW4 9BP, **1180**

RUSCHA, Ed, HON RA, c/o Royal Academy of Arts, **86**

Ruyter, Lisa, Courtesy of Alan Cristea Gallery, 31 & 34 Cork Street, London W1S 3NU, **444, 447**

Ryan, Anne, 1A Kempsford Road, London SE11 4NU, **947**

RYAN, Thomas, HON MEMBER EX OFFICIO PPRHA, Robertstown Lodge, Robertstown, Ashbourne, County Meath, Ireland, **1244**

Rybolt, Brian, 20 Godwin Road, Hastings, East Sussex TN35 5JR, **1037**

Ryle, David, 35A Bouverie Road, London N16 0AH, **1021**

Ryu, Changwoo, 7 Marlowe House, 147 Durham Road, London SW20 0DQ, **1005**

S

Saari, Paul, P. O. Box 1001, 2060 York Rd, Niagara-on-the-Lake, Ontario, L0S 1J0, Canada, **1086, 1099**

Sadikoglu, Handan, 15 Castle Road, Weybridge, Surrey KT13 9QP, **370**

Salliander, Issa, Flat 31, 30 Eagle Wharf Road, London
NI 7EH, **1159**

SANDLE, Prof. Michael, RA, Courtesy of Royal British
Society of Sculptors, 108 Old Brompton Road, London
SW7 3RA, **99, 357, 358, 723, 724, 725**

Saull, Martin, 31 Tollgate Avenue, Redhill, Surrey RH1 5HR,
334

Saunders, Glyn, 53 Trinity Rise, London SW2 2QP, **1061**

Schelenz, Silke, 94 Denmark Street, The Orchards, Diss,
Norfolk IP22 4LF, **338**

Scott, Ned, 8 Rectory Grove, London SW4 0EA, **817, 821**

Scrivener, Tony, Crandel, 28 Beaufoys Avenue, Ferndown,
Dorset BH22 9RH, **1195**

SCULLY, Sean, RA, Courtesy of Timothy Taylor Gallery,
15 Carlos Place, London W1K 2EX, **56**

Seeley, Eric, 4 Irwin Road, Bedford MK40 3UL, **1058**

Sellars, Margaret, 47A Gibbon Road, Kingston upon Thames,
Surrey KT2 6AD, **162, 335**

Senoj, Mit, c/o Paul Stolper Gallery, 31 Museum Street,
London WC1A 1LH, **548, 551**

Seow, James, 12C Jackson Road, London N7 6EJ, **151**

SETCH, Terry, RA, 111 Plymouth Road, Penarth, Vale of
Glamorgan CF64 5DF, **42, 52, 53, 54, 55, 119**

Seto, Andrew, 13 Mattison Road, London N4 1BG, **648**

Shaw, Phil, c/o Rebecca Hossack Gallery, 2A Conway Street,
London W1T 6BA, **1024**

Shaw, Robert John, 4 Barrass Square, Staithes, Saltburn-by-
the-Sea, Cleveland TS13 5DF, **1115**

Sheppard, Maurice, 33 St Martins Park, Crowhill,
Haverfordwest, Pembrokeshire SA61 2HP, **1138, 1186**

Shiomi, Nana, 96A Greenvale Road, London SE9 1PF, **262,
274**

Shread, Peter, 6 Clark Street, Stourbridge, West Midlands
DY8 3UF, **381**

Sillito, Adam, North Haven, 111A Mycenae Road, London
SE3 7RX, **1002**

Silverwood Taylor, Caroline, 13 Lords Hill, Coleford,
Gloucestershire GL16 8BG, **1009**

Simon, Francesca, c/o Beardsmore Gallery, 22-24 Prince of
Wales Road, London NW5 3LG, **391**

Sims, Ron, Bugle Cottage, 123 Tilkey Road, Coggeshall,
Essex CO6 1QN, **656, 671**

Slattery, Nicola, North Barn, Mill Road, Alburgh, Harleston,
Norfolk IP20 0DS, **1085**

Sleigh, Bronwen, Flat 2/2, 5 Wilton Drive, Glasgow G20 6RW,
988

Smith, Bridget, 43 Sharon Gardens, London E9 7RX, **1012**

Smith, James, 34 Stanhope Road, Northampton NN2 6JX,
904, 907

Smith, Peter S., 36 Bicester Road, Richmond, Surrey
TW9 4QN, **300, 374**

Smith, Richard, c/o Flowers Gallery, 82 Kingsland Road,
London E2 8DP, **537, 538**

Smith, Wendy, 2 Little Brownings, London SE23 3XJ, **764**

Smithey, Lisa, Flat 2, 5 Peckham High Street, London
SE15 5EB, **1066**

Sole, Terry, 178 Mortimer Street, Herne Bay, Kent CT6 5DT,
1222

Song, Yifei, 309 Elm Tree Court, Elm Tree Road, London
NW8 9JT, **818**

Southall, Tim, 67 Emanuel House, 18 Rochester Row,
London SW1P 1BS, **255**

Souto Moura, Eduardo, Souto Moura Arquitectos, S.A.,
Rua do Aleixo, nº53, 1ºA Esq., Porto 4150-043, Portugal,
823

Spencer, Anthony, 55 Southbrook Road, London SE12 8LJ,
1144

Spens, Peter, 3 Cranley Gardens, London N10 3AA, **403**

Stanford, Fianne, 85 High Street, Burnham-on-Crouch,
Essex CM0 8AH, **384**

Stanton Williams, 36 Graham Street, London N1 8GJ, **763,
765, 871, 924**

Stark, Ashley, 38 Morton Road, London N1 3BD, **376**

Stewart, David, 39 Featherstone Street, London EC1Y 8RE, **965**

STIBBON, Emma, RA, 30 Islington Road, Southville, Bristol
BS3 1QB, **49, 50, 57**

Stjernsward, Philippa, 181B Lavender Hill, London SW11 5TE, **883**

Stobart, Jane, 47 Potter Street, Harlow, Essex CM17 9AE, **287**

Stocker, Cathy, EVA Studio, 77 Steeds Road, London N10 1JB, **568**

Strainge, Celia May, 26 Highdown Road, Lewes, East Sussex BN7 1QE, **999**

Strupinski, Tom, 35 Mount Ararat Road, Richmond TW10 6PQ, **1126**

Studio 8 Architects, c/o C. J. Lim, 95 Greencroft Gardens, London NW6 3PG, **801, 810**

Studio Egret West, c/o Pauline Williams, 1 Compton Courtyard, 40 Compton Street, London EC1V 0BD, **859**

Sullivan, Benjamin, 8 Duddery Road, Haverhill, Suffolk CB9 8EA, **1225**

Sumner, Craig, 94 Caverswall Road, Blythe Bridge, Stoke-on-Trent, Staffordshire ST11 9BG, **1098**

Sutherland, Jack, 13 Canonsleigh Crescent, Leigh-on-Sea, Essex SS9 1RJ, **581**

Sutton, Linda, 192 Battersea Bridge Road, London SW11 3AE, **1124**

Sutton, Paul, First Floor, 25 Winchester Street, London SW1V 4NZ, **1238**

SUTTON, Philip, RA, 3 Morfa Terrace, Manorbier, Tenby, Pembrokeshire SA70 7TH, **703, 704, 705, 1087, 1197, 1198**

Sutton, Trevor, 5 The Colonnades, 105 Wilton Way, London E8 1BH, **879**

Swayne, Geraldine, 330B Old Ford Road, London E3 5TA, **1077**

T

Tabrizian, Mitra, The Wapping Project Bankside, 65A Hopton Street, London SE1 9LR, **961**

Takahashi, Lisa, 23 Highlands Road, Barnet, Hertfordshire EN5 5AA, **369**

Tarr, Michael, Pitch View, Howleigh, Blagdon Hill, Taunton, Somerset TA3 7SR, **1071**

Taylor, Rosie, c/o Deborah Taylor, 42 Vicarage Road, London SW14 8RU, **577**

Tearne, Mollie, 19 Walton Crescent, Oxford OX1 2JG, **1042, 1043**

Teusink, Marcia, 81 Clissold Crescent, London N16 9AS, **304**

Thomas, Glenny, 73 Marston Lane, Frome, Somerset BA11 4DG, **1219**

Thomas, Joseph, 403 The Mill, South Hall Street, Salford, Lancashire M5 4JH, **970**

Thomas, Nancy, 376 Court Road, Orpington, Kent BR6 9BX, **608**

Thual, Hannah, 217 Wilmot Street, London E2 0BY, **643**

Thurston, David, 1 North Castle Mews, Totnes, Devon TQ9 5NQ, **1015**

Till, Tobias, c/o TAG Fine Arts, Business Design Centre, 52 Upper Street, London N1 0QH, **288**

TILSON, Joe, RA, c/o Marlborough Fine Art, 6 Albemarle Street, London W1S 4BY, **113, 661, 662**, Courtesy of Alan Cristea Gallery, 31 & 34 Cork Street, London W1S 3NU, **208, 209, 210**

TINDLE, Dr David, RA, c/o The Redfern Gallery, 20 Cork Street, London W1S 3HL, **126, 130, 1125, 1132, 1201, 1252**

Tingle, Mike, 29 Applegarth Avenue, Newton Abbot, Devon TQ12 1RP, **254, 507**

Tizard, Lucas, 74 Westbourne Terrace, London W2 6QA, **998**

Tonkin, Paul, Top Flat, 30 The Gardens, London SE22 9QF, **566**

Torrance, Abbi, 118 Sunnyhill Road, London SW16 2UL, **617**

Torres Hernandez, Alberto, Flat 2, Peridot Court, 63 Virginia Road, London E2 7NF, **575**

Tournay-Godfrey, Delia, 2 Wimborne Avenue, Ipswich, Suffolk IP3 8QW, **1130**

Trushina, Margarita, Flat 3, 19 Pembridge Square, London W2 4EJ, **770**

Turk, Gavin, Live Stock Market, 415 Wick Lane, London E3 2JG, **940**

Turpin, Louis, 19 Udimore Road, Rye, East Sussex TN31 7DS, **1107**

Turrall-Clarke, Robert, Homestead Farmhouse, Chiddingfold, Godalming, Surrey GU8 4XS, **632**

U

Underwood, George, The White House, Limes Lane, Buxted, Uckfield, East Sussex TN22 4PB, **1240**

Ungureanu, Florin-Catalin, Flat 10 Dominic Court, 43 The Gardens, London SE22 9QR, **613**

Unwin, Phoebe, 32 Basterfield House, Golden Lane Estate, London EC1Y 0TP, **637**

V

Vanderwerf, Tina, Felix Timmermanslaan 5, Rosmalen 5242 EH, Netherlands, **1016**

Vorobyev, Alexander, 3 Ashby Mews, London SW2 5EP, **887, 1116**

W

Waddington, Geri, 51 Sunningdale, Orton Waterville, Peterborough PE2 5UB, **301**

Waldron, Dylan, 2 Hallaton Road, Slawston, Nr Market Harborough, Leicestershire LE16 7UA, **1164**

Walker, John, c/o Advanced Graphics London, 32 Long Lane, London SE1 4AY, **146**

Wardle, Adam, Flat 8, 148 Church Road, London SE19 2NT, **279**

Warsop, Anna, 98 Cotswold Road, Windmill Hill, Bristol BS3 4NS, **319**

Waterhouse, Jane, 245 High Street, Arlesey, Bedfordshire SG15 6TA, **405**

WATSON, Arthur, HON MEMBER EX OFFICIO PRSA, 5 Melville Street, Perth PH1 5PY, **282**

Waugh, Louise, 4 Wellington Terrace, Wiveliscombe, Somerset TA4 2NP, **1070**

Webster, Stephen, 119 Catherine Way, Batheaston, Bath BA1 7PB, **884**

Wells, Robert E., 2 Ruskin Road, Eastbourne, East Sussex BN20 9AY, **1207, 1208**

WHISHAW, Anthony, RA, 7A Albert Place, London W8 5PD, **31, 60, 123, 124**

Wiener, Jenny, Studio 160, 8 Shepherds Market, London W1J 7JY, **259, 420**

Wilde, Helen, 16A Annesley Road, London SE3 0JX, **1121**

WILDING, Alison, RA, c/o Karsten Schubert, 5-8 Lower
  John Street, Golden Square, London WIF 9DR, **880, 881**
WILKINSON, Chris, OBE RA, Wilkinson Eyre Architects,
  33 Bowling Green Lane, London ECIR OBJ, **789, 793, 846**,
  Wilkinson Design Studio, 52 Park Hall Road, London
  SE21 8BW, **906**
Williams, Annie, 31 Ellington Street, London N7 8PN, **503**
Williams, Karen, 11 Churchfield Road, Reigate, Surrey
  RH2 9RH, **165, 166**
Williams, Mandy, 13A Peak Hill Avenue, London SE26 4LG,
  1031
Williams, William Vaughan, Flat 2B, Lower Park Road,
  Brightlingsea, Essex CO7 OJS, **624**
Williams A'Court, Sue, 38 Park Avenue South, London
  N8 8LT, **1051**
Willingham, Roy, 22 Queen Anne Road, London E9 7AH,
  241, 242
Willoughby-Holland, Marisa, 35 Haydn Avenue, Purley,
  Surrey CR8 4AG, **1060**
Wilson, Birgitta, 9 The Quarter, Cranbrook Road,
  Staplehurst, Tonbridge, Kent TNI2 OEP, **446**
Wilson, Kate, 7 Hotham Road, London SWI9 IBS, **1241**
WILSON, Prof. Richard, RA, 44 Banyard Road, London
  SE16 2YA, **41, 109, 815**
Winkelman, Joseph, 69 Old High Street, Oxford OX3 9HT,
  251, 452
Winstanley, Paul, Courtesy of Alan Cristea Gallery,
  31 & 34 Cork Street, London WIS 3NU, **495**
WOODROW, Bill, RA, c/o Royal Academy of Arts, **732, 956**
Woods, Richard, Courtesy of Alan Cristea Gallery,
  31 & 34 Cork Street, London WIS 3NU, **435**
Woodward, Jooney, 43D Colebrooke Row, London NI 8AF,
  1019
Wooster, Steven, 41 Colin Gardens, London NW9 6EL, **615**
Wormell, Jane, 81 Marlborough Road, London N22 8NL, **1193**
WRAGG, John, RA, 6 Castle Lane, Devizes, Wiltshire
  SNIO IHJ, **890, 891, 892, 893, 894, 945**
Wraith, Robbie, The Old School House, The Green, Holton,
  Oxford OX33 IPS, **1063, 1083**

Wright, Simon, 41 Melton Road, Wymondham, Norfolk
NR18 0DB, **1154, 1174**
Wright, William, 13 Kilmorie Road, London SE23 2SS, **556**
Wroe, Stuart, Jackdaw Cottage, 15 Gargrave Road, Broughton,
Nr Skipton, North Yorkshire BD23 3AQ, **1145**
Wu, Charles K. H., 13 Munster Square, London NW1 3PH,
805
Wylie, Peter, 20A Court Road, London SE9 5NW, **1234**
Wylie, Rose, c/o Tate, **15**

X   Xiangming, Cheung, c/o Tanya Baxter Contemporary,
436 Kings Road, London SW10 0LJ, **1229**

Y   Yahya, Kim, 237 North Road, London SW19 1TP, **606**
Yuasa, Katsutoshi, c/o TAG Fine Arts, Business Design
Centre, 52 Upper Street, London N1 0QH, **494**

Z   Zac-Varghese, Sagen, Flat 1A, 1 Wedderburn Road, London
NW3 5QR, **553**
Zec, Donald, Flat 10, Redlynch Court, 70 Addison Road,
London W14 8JG, **626**
Zhong, Yunshu, 18A Cannon Hill Lane, London SW20 9EP,
612
Ziverts, Ylva, 10 Rue Libération, Enghien-les-Bains 95880,
France, **659**

Supporting the Royal Academy

Supporting the Royal Academy

The Royal Academy of Arts receives no revenue funding from government and is entirely reliant on self-generated income and charitable support.
Registered Charity No. 1125383

The Royal Academy Trust
Registered Charity No. 1067270

The Royal Academy Trust was founded in 1981 to receive, invest and disburse funds given in support of the Royal Academy of Arts. Since then the Trust has raised an endowment fund that now amounts to nearly £26 million, the income from which helps to finance the Academy's charitable activities, and has obtained funding totalling almost £60 million for capital projects, including the creation of the Sackler Wing of Galleries. The recent phase of works included the restoration of and improvements to the Main Galleries, the Annenberg Courtyard and the John Madejski Fine Rooms, open to the public for exhibitions from the newly catalogued and conserved Royal Academy Permanent Collection.

Become a Patron

The Royal Academy's Patrons Groups form a vital source of income in the absence of public funding. The Patrons Groups maintain and develop the Academy's internationally renowned exhibition programme; fund education projects for children, families and people with special needs; provide scholarships and bursaries for art students in the Royal Academy Schools; and help to conserve the Academy's unique Permanent Collection.

Further information on charitable giving to the Royal Academy can be obtained from Karin Grundy, Head of Patrons, on 020 7300 5671, or from Kathleen Hearst, American Associates of the Royal Academy Trust, 555 Madison Avenue, Suite 1300, New York, NY 10022, USA.

Leaving a gift to the Royal Academy in your will

If you would like to protect the Royal Academy so that future generations can enjoy its treasures, please consider leaving a gift to the Academy in your will.

A gift can be a sum of money, a specific item or a share of what is left after you have provided for your family and friends. Any gift, large or small, is greatly appreciated and will help us to continue our tradition of artistic excellence into the future.

For more information please contact Emma Warren-Thomas on 020 7300 5677, or at legacies@royalacademy.org.uk

Corporate opportunities

Since its foundation in 1768 the Academy has remained both independent and self-supporting, receiving no government funding for its exhibitions or education programmes.

The Academy has successfully led the fields of arts sponsorship, corporate membership and corporate entertaining for around 30 years. Together, these aspects make a significant financial contribution, enabling the Academy to maintain both the excellent artistic reputation for which it is known and its home, Burlington House, and to fulfil the role that it plays in the cultural life of this country.

Since 1979 the Academy has worked with over 200 sponsors in a range of areas, including exhibitions, education, fundraising events and the Royal Academy Schools. The Project Giving team also looks after 60 Corporate Members who enjoy numerous benefits for their staff, clients and community partners.

Sponsorship and corporate membership can offer companies:

- Priority booking of and exclusive entertaining in the Royal Academy's suite of eighteenth-century Fine Rooms, for business presentations, breakfasts or dinners combined with private views of exhibitions.
- Comprehensive crediting on all publicity material and involvement with press and promotions campaigns (sponsorship only).
- Invitations to prestigious Royal Academy corporate and social events.
- Special passes for unlimited entry to all Royal Academy exhibitions.
- Free entry for employees; behind-the-scenes tours; lectures and workshops for staff and their families.
- Regular monitoring and evaluation.
- A dedicated team of experienced staff to manage every aspect of sponsorship, corporate membership and corporate entertaining.

Further details are available from the Project Giving Office on 020 7300 5629/5979.

Royal Academy Trust

Registered Charity No. 1067270

American Associates of the Royal Academy Trust

Japanese Committee of Honour

Corporate Members

Mr Nobuyuki Idei (J Concept) and Mrs Idei

Mr Yoshitoshi Kitajima (Dai Nippon Printing Co Ltd) and Mrs Kitajima

Mr Shinzo Maeda and Mrs Maeda

Mr Yoshihiko Miyauchi (ORIX Corporation) and Mrs Miyauchi

Mr Yuzaburo Mogi (Kikkoman Corporation) and Mrs Mogi

Mrs Yoshiko Mori (Mori Building Co Ltd)

Mr Takeo Obayashi (Obayashi Corporation) and Mrs Obayashi

Mr Nobutada Saji (Suntory Limited) and Mrs Saji

Mrs Takako Suzuki

Mr Toichi Takenaka (Takenaka Corporation) and Mrs Takenaka

Mr Yuzo Yagi (Yagi Tsusho Ltd) and Mrs Yagi

Patrons

Mr Hiroaki Fujii (Chair) and Mrs Fujii

Prof Tadao Ando HON RA and Mrs Ando

Mr Akito Arima and Mrs Arima

Mr Shinji Fukukawa and Mrs Fukukawa

Mr Peter Highland

Mr and Mrs Nobuyuki Idei

Prof Arata Isozaki HON RA and Mrs Isozaki

Mr and Mrs Yoshitoshi Kitajima

Mr and Mrs Shinzo Maeda

Mr and Mrs Yoshihiko Miyauchi

Mr and Mrs Yuzaburo Mogi

Mrs Minoru Mori

Mr Hideo Morita and Mrs Morita

Mr Koichi Nezu and Mrs Nezu

Mr and Mrs Takeo Obayashi

Mr and Mrs Nobutada Saji

Mrs Yu Serizawa

Mr Yoji Shimizu and Mrs Shimizu

Mr Masayoshi Son and Mrs Son

Mr Jonathan Stone and Mrs Stone

Mrs Tadao Suzuki

Mrs Yuko Tadano

Mr Hideya Taida HON CBE and Mrs Taida

Mr Shuji Takashina and Mrs Takashina

Mr Tsuneharu Takeda and Mrs Takeda

Mr Hiroyasu Tomita and Mrs Tomita

Mr and Mrs Yuzo Yagi

Mrs Yasuko Yamazaki

Mrs Yu Serizawa (Director)

Royal Academy Supporters

The Trustees of the Royal Academy Trust are grateful to all its donors for their continued loyalty and generosity. They would like to extend their thanks to all those who have made a significant commitment, past and present, to the galleries, the exhibitions, the conservation of the Permanent Collection, the Library collections, the Royal Academy Schools, the Learning programme and other specific appeals.

Major Benefactors

HM The Queen
Her Majesty's Government
The 29th May 1961 Charitable Trust
The Aldama Foundation
The American Associates of the Royal Academy Trust
The Annenberg Foundation
Barclays Bank
BAT Industries plc
Sir David and Lady Bell
The late Tom Bendhem
The late Brenda M Benwell-Lejeune
John Frye Bourne
British Telecom
The Brown Foundation
John and Susan Burns
Mr Raymond M Burton CBE
Sir Trevor Chinn CVO and Lady Chinn
The Trustees of the Clore Foundation
The John S Cohen Foundation
Sir Harry and Lady Djangoly
The Dulverton Trust
Alfred Dunhill Limited
The John Ellerman Foundation
The Eranda Foundation
Ernst & Young
Esso UK plc
Esmée Fairbairn Charitable Trust
The Fidelity UK Foundation
The Foundation for Sports and the Arts

Friends of the Royal Academy
Jacqueline and Michael Gee
The Getty Grant Programme
Mr Thomas Gibson
Glaxo Holdings plc
Diane and Guilford Glazer
Mr and Mrs Jack Goldhill
Maurice and Laurence Goldman
The Horace W Goldsmith Foundation
HRH Princess Marie-Chantal of Greece
Mr and Mrs Jocelin Harris
The Philip and Pauline Harris Charitable Trust
The Charles Hayward Foundation
Heritage Lottery Fund
IBM United Kingdom Limited
The Idlewild Trust
Lord and Lady Jacobs
The JP Jacobs Charitable Trust
The Japan Foundation
Gabrielle Jungels-Winkler Foundation
Mr and Mrs Donald Kahn
The Lillian Jean Kaplan Foundation
The Kresge Foundation
The Samuel H Kress Foundation
The Kirby Laing Foundation
The Lankelly Foundation
The late Mr John S Latsis

Patrons of the Royal Academy

In recent years the Royal Academy has established several Patrons Groups to encourage the regular and committed support of individuals who believe in the Royal Academy's mission to promote the widest possible understanding and enjoyment of the visual arts.

The Royal Academy is delighted to thank all its Patrons for generously supporting exhibitions, Learning, the Royal Academy Schools, the Permanent Collection and Library, and Anglo-American initiatives over the past year, and for assisting in the general upkeep of the Academy, with donations of £1,500 and more.

Royal Academy Patrons

Chair	Robert Suss

Platinum Patrons	Celia and Edward Atkin CBE	Mr Denis Korotkov-Koganovich
	Mr and Mrs Christopher Bake	Mr and Mrs Jake Shafran
	Mr and Mrs Patrick Doherty	David and Sophie Shalit
	Ms Ghizlan El Glaoui	

Gold Patrons	Christopher and Alex Courage	Sir Keith and Lady Mills
	Mr and Mrs Andrew Higginson	Jean and Geoffrey Redman-Brown
	Mrs Elizabeth Hosking	Mrs Stella Shawzin
	Miss Joanna Kaye	Mr Kevin Sneader and Ms Amy Muntner
	Lady Rayne Lacey	Jane Spack
	Jacqueline and Marc Leland	David Stileman
	The Licensing Company, London	Mrs Elyane Stilling
	Sir Sydney Lipworth QC and Lady Lipworth CBE	Mr and Mrs Pierre Winkler
	Mr and Mrs Ronald Lubner	Mr Robert John Yerbury

Silver Patrons	Lady Agnew	Mr Nigel Boardman
	Miss H J C Anstruther	Eleanor E Brass
	Lord Ashburton	Mrs Gary Brass
	Mr and Mrs Simon Bamber	Mr and Mrs Richard Briggs OBE
	Jane Barker	Mrs Marcia Brocklebank
	Ms Catherine Baxendale	Sir Francis Brooke Bt
	The Duke of Beaufort	Mrs Joyce Brotherton
	Mrs J K M Bentley, Summers Art Gallery	Lady Brown
		Jeremy Brown

Lord Browne of Madingley
Mr Martin Burton
Mr F A A Carnwath CBE
Jean and Eric Cass
Sir Charles and Lady Chadwyck-
    Healey
Sir Trevor Chinn CVO and Lady
    Chinn
Mr and Mrs George Coelho
Denise Cohen Charitable Trust
Sir Ronald Cohen
Ms Linda Cooper
Mark and Cathy Corbett
Mr and Mrs Ken Costa
Julian Darley and Helga Sands
The Countess of Dartmouth
Mr Daniel Davies
Peter and Andrea De Haan
The de Laszlo Foundation
Professor and Mrs John Deanfield
Mrs Anita Dinkin
Dr Anne Dornhorst
Lord Douro
Mr and Mrs Jim Downing
Ms Noreen Doyle
Janet and Maurice Dwek
Mrs Sheila Earles
Lord and Lady Egremont
Bryan Ferry
Mr Sam Fogg
Mrs Rosamund Fokschaner
Mrs Jocelyn Fox
Mrs Marion F Foster
Mrs Anthony Foyle
Mr and Mrs Eric Franck
Mr Simon Freakley
Arnold Fulton
The Lord Gavron CBE
Jacqueline and Jonathan Gestetner
Lady Getty
Mr Mark Glatman
Lady Gosling
Mr Stephen Gosztony
Piers Gough CBE RA
Mr Gavin Graham
Mrs Mary Graves

HRH Princess Marie-Chantal of
    Greece
Mrs Margaret Guitar
Mr James Hambro
Sir Ewan and Lady Harper
Mrs Melanie Harris
Richard and Janeen Haythornthwaite
Sir John Hegarty and Miss Philippa
    Crane
Michael and Morven Heller
Lady Heseltine
Mr and Mrs Alan Hobart
Mr Philip Hudson
Mr and Mrs Jon Hunt
Mrs Deanna Ibrahim
S Isern-Feliu
Mrs Caroline Jackson
Mr Derek Jacobson
Mr Michael Jacobson
Sir Martin and Lady Jacomb
Mrs Raymonde Jay
Fiona Johnstone
Mr Nicholas Jones
Mrs Ghislaine Kane
Dr Elisabeth Kehoe
Mr Duncan Kenworthy OBE
Princess Jeet Khemka
Mr and Mrs Naguib Kheraj
Mr D H Killick
Mr and Mrs James Kirkman
Mrs Aboudi Kosta
Mr and Mrs Herbert Kretzmer
Norman A Kurland and Deborah
    A David
Joan H Lavender
Mr George Lengvari and Mrs Inez
    Lengvari
Lady Lever of Manchester
Mr Peter Lloyd
Miss R Lomax-Simpson
The Marquess of Lothian
The Hon Mrs Virginia Lovell
Mr and Mrs Henry Lumley
Mrs Josephine Lumley
Mrs Sally Lykiardopulo
Gillian McIntosh
Andrew and Judith McKinna

Contemporary Circle Patrons

Charitable Trust
The Dovehouse Trust
The Gilbert and Eileen Edgar Foundation
The John Ellerman Foundation
The Eranda Foundation
Lucy Mary Ewing Charitable Trust
The Margery Fish Charity
The Flow Foundation
The Garfield Weston Foundation
Gatsby Charitable Foundation
The Golden Bottle Trust
The Gordon Foundation
Sue Hammerson Charitable Trust
The Charles Hayward Foundation
Heritage Lottery Fund
Hiscox
Holbeck Charitable Trust
The Harold Hyam Wingate Foundation
The Ironmongers' Company
The Emmanuel Kaye Foundation
The Kindersley Foundation
The de Laszlo Foundation
The David Lean Foundation
The Leche Trust
The Leverhulme Trust
The Maccabaeans
The McCorquodale Charitable Trust
The Machin Foundation
The Paul Mellon Centre
The Paul Mellon Estate
The Mercers' Company
Margaret and Richard Merrell Foundation
The Millichope Foundation
The Mondriaan Foundation
The Monument Trust
The Henry Moore Foundation
The Mulberry Trust
The J Y Nelson Charitable Trust

The Old Broad Street Charity Trust
The Peacock Charitable Trust
The Pennycress Trust
PF Charitable Trust
The Stanley Picker Charitable Trust
The Pidem Fund
The Edith and Ferdinand Porjes Charitable Trust
Mr and Mrs J A Pye's Charitable Settlement
Rayne Foundation
The Reed Foundation
T Rippon & Sons (Holdings) Ltd
Rootstein Hopkins Foundation
The Rose Foundation
Schroder Charity Trust
The Sellars Charitable Trust
The Archie Sherman Charitable Trust
Paul Smith and Pauline Denyer-Smith
The South Square Trust
Spencer Charitable Trust
Oliver Stanley Charitable Trust
Peter Storrs Trust
Strand Parishes Trust
The Joseph Strong Frazer Trust
The Swan Trust
Thaw Charitable Trust
Sir Jules Thorn Charitable Trust
The Bruce Wake Charity
Celia Walker Art Foundation
Warburg Pincus International LLC
Weinstock Fund
Wilkinson Eyre Architects
The Spencer Wills Trust
The Maurice Wohl Charitable Foundation
The Wolfson Foundation
The Worshipful Company of Painter-Stainers

American Associates of the Royal Academy Trust

Friends of the Royal Academy

Patron: HRH The Duke of Edinburgh KG KT
Chairman: Ron Zeghibe

Join the Friends of the Royal Academy and enjoy free entry to all RA exhibitions, plus...

- Previews of exhibitions before they open to the public at Friends Preview Days
- Bring one adult family guest and up to four family children under 16 to any exhibition for free
- Use of the Keeper's House (opening Autumn 2013)
- Access to a programme of Friends events
- Receive the quarterly *RA Magazine*
- Keep up to date with the Friends e-news, packed with events, news and offers

To become a Friend

Visit	The Friends desk in the Front Hall
Go to	www.royalacademy.org.uk/friends
Call	020 7300 5664
E-mail	friend.enquiries@royalacademy.org.uk
Or write to	Friends Office
	Royal Academy of Arts
	FREEPOST 33WD 1057
	Piccadilly
	London W1E 6YZ

Royal Academy Corporate Membership Scheme

Registered Company No. 2216104

Launched in 1988, the Royal Academy's Corporate Membership Scheme has proved highly successful. Corporate Membership offers company benefits to staff, clients and community partners and access to the Academy's facilities and resources. The outstanding support we receive from companies via the scheme is vital to the continuing success of the Academy and we thank all our Members for their valuable support and continued enthusiasm.

Premier Level Members

- A T Kearney Limited
- Barclays plc
- Bird & Bird
- Catlin Group Limited
- CBRE
- Christie's
- Deutsche Bank AG
- FTI Consulting
- GlaxoSmithKline plc
- Insight Investment
- JM Finn & Co
- Jones Lang LaSalle
- JTI
- KPMG
- Linklaters
- Neptune Investment Management
- Schroders Private Banking
- Smith & Williamson
- Sotheby's

Corporate Members

- The Boston Consulting Group UK LLP
- British American Tobacco
- Brunswick
- Bupa
- Capital International Limited
- Clifford Chance LLP
- Essex Court
- F & C Asset Management plc
- GAM
- La Mania
- Lazard
- Lindsell Train
- Lloyds TSB Private Banking
- Lubbock Fine Chartered Accountants
- Marie Curie
- Moelis & Company
- Oracle Capital Group
- The Royal Society of Chemistry
- Slaughter and May
- Tanya Baxter Contemporary
- Tiffany & Co.
- Trowers & Hamlins
- UBS
- Vision Capital Limited
- Weil, Gotshal & Manges

Associate Members

- All Nippon Airways
- Bank of America Merrill Lynch
- BNP Paribas
- Bloomberg LP
- Bonhams 1793 Ltd
- Credit Agricole CIB
- Ernst & Young
- Generation Investment Management LLP
- Heidrick & Struggles
- John Lewis Partnership
- Morgan Stanley
- Pentland Group plc
- Realty Insurances Limited
- Rio Tinto
- Sykes & Sons Limited
- Timothy Sammons Fine Art Agents

Sponsors of Past Exhibitions

The President and Council of the Royal Academy would like to thank the following sponsors and benefactors for their generous support of major exhibitions during the last ten years:

A T Kearney
ABNAMRO
Akkök Group of Companies
American Associates of the Royal Academy Trust
American Express
Aygaz
Bank of America
The Bank of New York Mellon
Bastyan
BBC Radio 3
Blain Southern
Blavatnik Family Foundation
Blueprint
BNP Paribas
British American Tobacco
Canon
Carlsberg UK Ltd
Castello di Reschio
Christie's
Classic FM
Corus
J F Costopoulos Foundation
Country Life
Cox & Kings
The Daily Telegraph
Daniel Katz Gallery
Danske Bank
Guy Dawson
Deutsche Bank AG
Edwards Wildman
E.ON
Ernst & Young
Eurohypo AG

Farrow & Ball
Fidelity Foundation
Lucy Flemming McGrath
Foster + Partners
Garanti Bank
Glasgow Museums
GlaxoSmithKline
Goldman Sachs International
The Great Britain Sasakawa Foundation
Guardian
Hauser & Wirth
The Hellenic Foundation
Hungarofest
The Independent
Insight Investment
The Japan Foundation
Lassa Tyres
A G Leventis Foundation
Harvey and Allison McGrath
Mexico Tourism Board
Mizuho International plc
Stavros Niarchos Foundation
Novo Nordisk
OAK Foundation Denmark
OTP Bank
Pemex
RA Exhibition Patrons Group
Region Holdings
Simon and Virginia Robertson
Sotheby's
The Spectator
Spoonfed
Terra Foundation

Time Out
Toshiba International Foundation
UBS Wealth Management

Villa Budapest
Walker Morris
Welcome to Yorkshire

Other sponsors (sponsors of events, publications and other items in the past five years)

Carlisle Group plc
Country Life
Derwent Valley Holdings plc
John Doyle Construction
Dresdner Kleinwort Wasserstein
Goldman Sachs International
Gome International
Gucci Group
Rob van Helden
Hines

Michael Hopkins & Partners
IBJ International plc
Martin Krajewski
Marks & Spencer
Morgan Stanley Dean Witter
Newton Investment Management
Prada
Radisson Edwardian Hotels
Richard and Ruth Rogers
The Wine Studio

Royal Academy Schools

The Royal Academy Schools provide the only three-year postgraduate course in Fine Art in the United Kingdom. The criteria for acceptance are positive commitment and a convincing potential for creative development. This is a small, exceptional school with a challenging atmosphere of experimentation and strong sense of identity.

The Schools attract a comprehensive range of visiting tutors, both practitioners and theorists, and there exists within the studios an ongoing atmosphere of critical debate and forward-looking inquiry.

The traditional forms of painting, sculpture and printmaking are pursued alongside such newer media as digital printing in a state-of-the-art Epson suite and with facilities for photography and video.

There are no fees and students are assisted financially in a limited way by means of a variety of awards, prizes and travel bursaries.

The Schools' central-London location and close proximity to the remarkable international-standard exhibition programme of the Royal Academy in Burlington House greatly enhance the rich cultural and educational environment that exists here.

Library

The Library of the Royal Academy is for the use of its Members, staff and students, and is open for specialist research by appointment.

Telephone: 020 7300 5737
E-mail: library@royalacademy.org.uk

AGBI

Artists' General Benevolent Institution
Burlington House
Piccadilly
London wij obb

Patron: HRH The Prince of Wales

Founded in 1814 by J M W Turner, the AGBI provides help to professional artists and their dependants in time of trouble.
    Funds are always needed and donations of any amount are gratefully received and acknowledged. Cheques should be sent to the Secretary at the above address.

Registered Charity No. 212667
Contact: 020 7734 1193
www.agbi.org.uk

Compiled by Natalie Bouloudis, Lorna Burn,
    Edith Devaney, Daniel Fabris,
    Natalie Gibbons, Louisa Joseph,
    Meredith Moore, Paul Sirr, Jessica Smith
Production by Abbie Coppard and Luke Hoyland
Designed by Adam Brown_01.02
Printed by Tradewinds

Published by RA Publications
Royal Academy of Arts
Piccadilly
London W1J 0BD

On the cover:
Grayson Perry RA
The Annunciation of the Virgin Deal, 2012 (detail)
Wool, cotton, acrylic, polyester and silk tapestry,
200 × 400 cm.
Courtesy the artist and Victoria Miro, London
© Grayson Perry. Photography © Stephen White.